THE ULTIMATI

WORK EXPERIENCE GUIDE

UniAdmissions

ISBN: 978-1-915091-21-5

Published by RAR Medical Services Limited
www.uniadmissions.co.uk
info@uniadmissions.co.uk
Tel: +44 (0) 208 068 0438

ABOUT THE AUTHOR

Bianca is a trainee doctor - affiliated with the University of Bristol. She's worked for many years as an admissions coach for medicine in the UK specifically - and has an expertise in work experience programmes for medics in the UK.

She completed four medical work experiences prior to starting as a medic in Europe and Africa, and teaches from experience as a peer and mentor to numerous aspiring doctors every year.

Outside of her medical work, Bianca enjoys providing pastoral support to new and prospective medical students and organises charity runs and sporting events in the UK and Europe.

THE ULTIMATE MEDICAL WORK EXPERIENCE GUIDE

BIANCA VAN BINSBERGEN

FOREWORD

Congratulations on your decision to pursue your interest in medicine, both as a degree and a career. Medicine is a very broad subject, branching from clinical practice to research to global health. You are sure to find an area of medicine that interests and challenges you.

Medical work experience is the first step in this journey. It is an opportunity for you to explore the medical field; what medicine entails as a career, what the environment is that you are likely to work in and what your lifestyle as a doctor may look like.

Your medical work experience will likely be your first exposure to what medicine is really like. It is very different to what your favourite hospital-based TV dramas have told you. The hours are long and the work is difficult and emotionally-tolling, but you get to work in a career that is different to any other career out there, and you get to do so in a team of people that may become your closest friends.

Many people find work experience very different to what they expected; but what you make of your time experiencing the medical world first-hand will play a crucial role in your decision to continue pursuing medicine or not. Medicine – as a degree and as a career – is not right for everyone, but hopefully your medical work experience will help you decide if it is right for you.

HOW TO USE THIS BOOK

The Ultimate Guide to Medical Work Experience is written as a guide to inform, prepare and support you through your experience of medical work experience.

Everything that you will need to know to successfully complete your medical work experience to be able to apply for medicine at UK universities can be found in this comprehensive guide.

You will find information on the basics of work experience, the importance of work experience, the decision-making process behind organising your work experience and completing the actual work experience itself. In addition to guiding you through the process of your work experience, this resource will also give you very valuable insight into the different medical specialties (and previous students' experiences in the specialties) as well as guiding you through your application process post-work experience.

Remember to have fun while you work hard. Good luck!

TABLE OF CONTENTS

THE BASICS

WHAT IS WORK EXPERIENCE?

It is important to have work experience prior to committing to any career, but it is essential to have for medicine. It allows individuals to understand the degree and career that they are interested in, and to acquaint themselves with the realities of the job they are aspiring to work in.

Medical work experience is a vital part of medical school applications, and for good reason; the idea of medicine is glamorised in more ways than one, and universities want to make sure that the students they are accepting and investing in understand the realities of a career in medicine.

More than just being a tick in the box for applications, medical work experience can help you decide if being a doctor is the right choice for you. Choosing a career is one of the most important decisions you will make; it will impact your studies at university, how you spend your working days and the people that you interact with on a daily basis.

"Medical work experience can provide valuable insight into what a career in medicine entails. It's a hugely rewarding and enlightening experience, empowering students to determine if this is a something that they want to pursue."

9

WHO NEEDS TO DO WORK EXPERIENCE?

Medical work experience is a requirement for applying to medical schools in the UK. Depending on which universities you are planning on applying to, their requirements in terms of length and type of work experience may differ. However, most universities do not set a minimum number of hours or days for which work experience needs to be undertaken, nor do they specify the type of work experience. There are some guidelines that universities tend to agree medical work experience needs to meet (see "What does good work experience look like?" on page 19 for more information).

"I'd highly recommend to anyone who is even considering medicine to undertake some medical work experience as it could completely change your mind and will help you make an informed decision."

Medical schools also tend to require that the relevant work experience is recent, which is outlined as having been done in the last two years at the time of application. Due to age restrictions to be able to undertake medical work experience – most require individuals to be 16 or older – this is not a requirement that people tend to struggle to meet. However, it is worth keeping in mind if applying after gap years, previous degrees or later on in life.

WHY IS WORK EXPERIENCE IMPORTANT?

Medical work experience allows individuals considering medicine to experience the day-to-day life of healthcare, to understand the expectations of those working in medicine and to decide whether this is the right path for you.

"Choosing to follow a career in medicine is a huge decision to make so it is incredibly useful to see the working environment first-hand and to consider whether you would be suited to it."

Many students that undertake medical work experience think that medicine is the right choice for them, and this work experience placement is often the first step in their journey to becoming a qualified and practicing doctor.

This is a wonderful experience to have, and being able to go into interviews and then begin medical school confident in your decision to pursue medicine is not to be understated. However, once some experience the reality of a career in healthcare, they will realise that maybe medicine is not the right choice for them, or that they first need to take some time to mature or pursue another interest before studying medicine sometime in the future. This is also a great realisation to have, and it allows for you to make this decision in an informed manner, while enabling someone else to pursue their dream of studying medicine right now.

Work experience take-aways are often discussed by students in their personal statements and drawn on as a talking point by universities in interviews. So it is important to not just complete the work experience and see it as just another requirement, but to get involved and reflect on what you have learnt about yourself and about medicine.

"Nowadays work experience is practically essential for all applicants to have in the run up to applying for medical school. This can be effectively showcased in your personal statement and asked about in interviews."

One of the most common responses regarding medical work experience is that it was nothing like they expected it to be – this is vitally important. Careers in medicine have become a focus on TV and in the media, and this has led to many misconceptions about what being a medical student and/or doctor is really like. The hours are long, the work is mentally exhausting and there is a lot of paperwork, but it is also a hugely rewarding career that will impact every area of your life. It's a degree and career that cannot be accurately depicted on a screen or in words, it needs to be experienced first-hand to make an informed decision and commitment.

"My week of work experience transformed my perspective on a career in medicine and provided me with realistic insight into the unique challenges life as a doctor poses on the individual."

Medicine is a long and challenging course, requiring countless hours of studying, many days at hands-on placement and a lifetime of learning. It is in your best interest to inform yourself as well as you can prior to embarking on this journey – and medical work experience is the most accurate portrayal of what to expect from a career in medicine.

WHERE SHOULD I DO MY WORK EXPERIENCE?

There are two main types of medical work experience that prospective students can have and should try to attain. The first is direct observation, which is more commonly referred to as 'shadowing'. This is the more common type of medical work experience that school students tend to have because of limitations on age, ability to undertake paid employment and restrictions due to school hours. The second type of work experience is working with others (i.e. hands-on) in a role involving service or caring for others. This type of work experience is strongly recommended, as it allows individuals to have an active role in their experience, rather than the more passive role of shadowing healthcare professionals. You can gain this type of experience in many different settings, of which most are voluntary but some may be paid. Some options are elderly care homes, hospices, special education schools, nurseries or volunteering to support services for people that are disabled or disadvantaged.

Work experience can be useful in many different forms. The most relevant to medicine is obviously within a medical field, for example through a local scheme to allow you to shadow a specific department within your local hospital. Another example of medical work experience may be at your local general practitioner or even at your pharmacy. Volunteering is also often very useful, both for the benefit of your learning and that you are providing support to a service that benefits from your volunteer work. Paid employment may also provide you with useful work experience, depending on the work and what exactly it is that you are doing.

However, most types of work in which you interact with people and work in teams will help you to develop your interpersonal skills – and while working as a waitress will not help you understand medicine better, it will make you a more well-rounded candidate for medicine.

The most important thing about work experience is to remember that it is about what you learn from it. This can be what you learn about yourself, what you learn about others and what you learn about medicine. There is very little merit in boasting about what you managed to see or what you managed to do on your placement. The main goals of your medical work experience is to gain a realistic understanding of a career in medicine entails, to learn about the delivery of effective care and to demonstrate attributes that you have and developed that will make you a good candidate to become a medical student.

A brief list of potential work experience options includes, but is not limited to, the following:

- Shadowing a department team at your local hospital
- Shadowing a GP at your local practice
- Shadowing healthcare professionals abroad
- Volunteering in a care home
- Volunteering to provide first aid
- Volunteering to assist disadvantaged individuals
- Paid work in a caring role
- Volunteering in the community or working in customer service – less relevant to medicine, but good to develop yourself as an individual

Universities are very understanding of the fact that sometimes it is not possible to secure medical work placements, and that this is often dependent on factors that are outside of your control, for example where you live or who you know or what school you go to. What is very important is that you can show that you have gained understanding of medicine as a degree and career; and if you can show that you have worked with what you have and managed to show your commitment to medicine already by trying your best to develop your understanding, this will set you ahead of your cohort.

There are many ways to broaden your understanding and fuel your interest in medicine, which I recommend you pursue regardless of which medical work experiences you manage to secure. Some of these include talking to practising or recently retired doctors about their career and immersing yourself in relevant reading around about the subject. Medical schools are interested in how you understand the values and attributes needed for good medical practice, and that you can demonstrate the ways in which you learnt these during work experience and through the aforementioned alternatives.

WHEN SHOULD I DO MY WORK EXPERIENCE?

Most universities require that medical work experience is done within the two years before applying to medical school. As the deadline for applications to medicine is mid-October, it is required that your work experience is done in the two years preceding this deadline. However, it is worth considering that many medical work experience schemes require individuals to be 16 years or older. Some students have managed to secure placements at 15 years old, but they report that they were unable to observe surgeries and attend some of the procedures that they would have been able to had they been 16 years old.

Ideally, the best timespan to undertake medical work experience is therefore between your 16th birthday and when you submit your applications. Keep in mind though, that you can begin looking for opportunities and even secure them before you are 16, but plan them for once you have turned 16. Many people find this quite helpful, as they find that school becomes quite busy around this time and while it is possible to find time to complete the placements, the time-consuming part of actually finding and securing the opportunities is completed.

HOW DO I GET WORK EXPERIENCE?

Use your work experience time to explore careers and specialties that you already have an interest in. The first decisions you need to make before you look for work experience is what kind of a placement you want to do and what the time period is that you would like to undertake the work experience during. Once you have decided this, you need to figure out what opportunities would be available to you locally, or alternatively, how far you are able to travel for your work experience placement.

When you start looking for your work experience placements, it helps to begin by talking to people that you know or who would be able to help you with this search. Most people use links that their school has, or that they know through family or friends. Due to these relationships, you may find that you are more successful in securing work experience placements locally. Obviously, this may not be what you have in mind or wanted to plan, but it is worth keeping in mind if you found that you were having trouble in securing a placement further from home. You could also try to use links that you have abroad, if you were keen to do so.

Emails and phone calls are the best ways to contact potential work experience opportunities to express interest and to apply for medical work experience. Remember to be patient and persevere if you don't hear back immediately – you will eventually hear back, so don't lose heart!

HOW MUCH WORK EXPERIENCE DO I NEED TO DO?

Most UK universities agree on the general advice that ideally prospective medical students should do at least 2 weeks of full-time (70 hours total) medical work experience to allow for sufficient exposure and enough time to gain an understanding of the breadth of medicine.

However, this is just a guideline, and as previously mentioned (see "Where should I do my work experience?" on page 13), some individuals may be able to secure placements more easily due to a variety of reasons. Universities are very aware of this discrepancy, and value individuals' initiative in doing their best to gain experience and insight to develop them as a person and future medical student, while informing themselves to be able to make their own educated decision.

"I was quite stressed about finding my medical work experience but I made sure that I had a range of places to do my work experience at as I wanted to boost my personal statement as much as possible. This included my local hospital, my local opticians, my local vets, my local GP and a week's worth of work experience in a care home."

It is also worth noting that there is not much value in repeating medical work experience placements. As a student still at school, what you are capable of doing and legally allowed to do on a medical work placement is limited. So, it is in your best interest to pursue different types of work experience placements in different departments with different teams so that you can make the most of your time on medical work experience – within your limitations.

If you are keen on a longer work experience, a voluntary caring role working with individuals that are disabled or disadvantaged or elderly would be the most beneficial for you, and for those that you are supporting.

WHERE IS WORK EXPERIENCE INCLUDED IN MY APPLICATION?

The main area that your work experience will be included in is your personal statement. This is a 4000-character piece that is your opportunity to reflect who you are, to sell yourself on why you are a good candidate for medicine and to show what you have done to explore your interest in the run up to medical school. For most students, this will be what you learnt during your medical work experience placements, so make sure that you learn from your experience and can talk about what you observed, rather than just say you did it.

"You can always draw on the things you learnt from your work experience when you write your personal statement, and relate them to qualities that doctors need."

University interviews are another opportunity to display what you have learnt from your work experience, alongside the other steps that you have taken to prepare yourself for the challenging degree you are aiming to embark on. Keep in mind that some universities (especially MMI-style interviews) may not specifically ask about your work experience, but rather about the challenges you faced. Many successful applicants quote that they were able to offer insight into their first-hand learning during work experience and believe this set them apart from the other applicants.

"This [work experience] was very useful in affirming my choice to apply for medicine, whilst also giving me insight that I could speak about in my personal statement and at my interview."

Some universities may also require that you attach or send a separate document outlining your work experience placements – in addition to your personal statement. This may be used as a way to confirm that you have completed the required placements, or to ascertain what you have gained from the placements prior to inviting you for interview or to guide interview questions and discussions.

"I mentioned surgery in my statement, which lead to my interviewer asking questions about healthcare practices in my home country in my interview, and I was able to comfortably and confidently offer personal insight."

WHAT DOES GOOD WORK EXPERIENCE LOOK LIKE?

'Good work experience' is quite subjective, and it will be dependent on what the specific universities you are applying to are looking for in a candidate. It is a good idea to consider the values of the universities you are interested in are, and what they state good doctors need to be capable of and have as attributes as students and as doctors.

For the most part, 'good work experience' is more about what you take from the experience in terms of learning and understanding, than the actual work experience itself. Work experience can take many forms, and can be any activity or life experience that would be useful and informative to you in your preparation to apply to and begin medical school. Your medical work experience will likely be your first exposure to the realities of a career in medicine, so make sure you use this opportunity to make an informed decision.

UK universities agree that 'good medical experience' is any experience that encompasses service or care, whilst allowing you to develop essential attributes required by doctors and gain a better understanding of the career itself.

"Most importantly, my medical experience exposed me to the realities of working in medicine from the professional's perspective for the first time. This was very useful in affirming my choice to apply for medicine."

WHAT DOES BAD WORK EXPERIENCE LOOK LIKE?

'Bad word experience' is less subjective than what comprises 'good work experience', but is still not as straightforward as being just 'bad work experience'. More often, it is all of your experiences put together and what you have gained from them, which makes your work experience 'good' or 'bad'.

The following are a few examples of what could constitute 'bad work experience', however you may need to use your judgement to decide if what you have planned for your work experience meets any of the 'bad work experience' criteria.

The main reason your medical work experience could be deemed 'bad' would be by completing various work experience placements that are very similar to one another. This will not allow you to gain as much as you could if you did placements that were broader, and will also not allow you to be exposed to different areas of healthcare.

Another reason could be if you completed your placements but didn't get involved in the placement to the best of your ability. A word of caution is warranted regarding getting too hands-on and potentially taking part in procedures that you are not trained to be and is therefore not safe. However, getting involved by talking to patients, making the most of opportunities to shadow different professionals and making sure you interact and engage with the placement will take your experience from being 'bad' to 'good'.

Often individuals may fall into the mindset of 'just getting through' their work experience placements. This can happen for a variety of reasons: from not feeling like you fit in (which is not true, they are probably just very busy!) to just wanting to finish the week and be able to tick work experience off for your application. Try to be intentional in not arriving late and not leaving at the first opportunity to do so. This time that you have to see what medicine entails is a privilege, and its value in helping you make this big decision is not to be understated. Be proactive and spend as much time as you can doing and seeing all that you can, so that you can appreciate all the aspects of a career in medicine.

Sometimes it is also very easy to get stuck on what you are able to see and how much you are able to do while you are on your work experience. While surgeries and various procedures may seem like the more exciting parts of the job – and the best parts to tell your family and friends about –, this is not where you are going to gain the most from your time doing work experience. As a prospective medical student, watching surgeries and interesting procedures is not going to make much sense, nor is it very reflective of a day in the life of a doctor if that is all you choose to observe. Spending time talking to the patients, asking the healthcare professionals questions and shadowing the doctors during the 'exciting' (surgeries, procedures, emergency calls) and the 'mundane' (rounds, lots of paperwork, prescribing medications) is going to allow you to make the most of your medical work experience.

WHAT ARE THE RIGHT WAYS TO DO WORK EXPERIENCE?

The general principles of what comprises good work experience is outlined in "What does good work experience look like?" on page 19. The following are actions that you can make sure to keep in the forefront of your mind during your work experience to do it 'right'.

Try and secure a variety of work experience opportunities. This may include hospitals, GP practices, volunteering, working with disabilities, working with people that are disadvantaged and many more.

Try to get as many placements as you can in different departments and specialties (as long as you have the time to do so and you making too many sacrifices to your school work). Focus on specialties or areas you are interested in if you can. But don't limit yourself to only your current interests, as they will most likely change!

Make the most of contacts that you have if they can help you to secure work experience opportunities or if they can suggest people to contact they may be able to help you to secure work experience. Approach previous students from your school, friends that have already done work experience or teachers/university counsellors. Use the people that you have access to, to further your understanding of the journey that you will be embarking on very soon.

Start early; you can get more done and get it out of the way before you get busy with your applications, course work and even your finals.

Be enthusiastic! It will help you to be invited to get more involved by the other healthcare professionals during your placement. It is very obvious when you're feigning interest, so make sure that you are being genuine!

Ask questions – the doctors will appreciate it when you are inquisitive and trying to get involved. Plus you will get much more out of your time on placement.

Try and shadow everyone in the team. Everyone has different jobs and responsibilities, but they all come together to deliver quality patient care when they work as a team. It is definitely worthwhile to see and understand the jobs of the other people in your multi-disciplinary team.

If you can see cool things: do! But not at the expense of speaking to patients and professionals – this is the part of your work experience from which you will gain the most if you are prepared to get involved and learn about medicine.

WHAT ARE THE WRONG WAYS TO DO WORK EXPERIENCE?

The general principles of what comprises bad work experience is outlined in "What does bad work experience look like?" on page 20. The following are reminders of what you should try not do in your work experience preparation and whilst completing your placements.

Try not to do multiple weeks or placements in the same department or in similar departments. As you are not yet a medical student, what you are able to do and observe is limited. So, use your time wisely and spend time in different departments and specialties with different teams to make the most of your time doing medical work experience.

Don't give up on finding or securing placements after a few unanswered emails or after a few potential opportunities that did not work out.

Don't start to look for and secure work experience opportunities too late. You don't want to be stressing about not having done placements or not having sorted them out when it comes to the time for your applications. You also don't want to have to cram your placements into the stressful period before your applications are due or around your exam season. Moral of the story: get your work experience planned and completed early.

Try not to prioritise work experience over exams and school work. While work experience is important, your school work and predicted grades (or final grades) are more important.

Don't do the bare minimum. Arriving late or leaving early is not going to help you get involved and gain a better understanding of the career, nor is it going to make the team that you are working with want to go above and beyond to help you have fun during your work experience. Make the most of this opportunity – get stuck in and gain experience! Also try not to act bored or uninterested during your work experience (it's so easy to pick up fake interest!).

Don't only shadow consultants. It may seem like the way to see the most and understand the job, but in reality, it will be many years until you become a consultant and before then you will have very different responsibilities. Consultants are also usually very busy, and so they may not be the best people to shadow if you want to ask questions and have discussions (this is not the case for all consultants, but generally, they are very busy). It is also great experience to observe the foundation doctors and registrars – they finished medical school much more recently, and they might be the best people to shadow to get involved and gain the best understanding of what to expect. You could even ask to shadow and/or work with one of the medical students if they are on the ward you are on – they'll be able to give you the best information and insight into medical school.

Try not to only be interested in the 'cool things'. Although these parts are great and very interesting to see, they are not the entirety (or even the majority) of what a job in medicine entails. A lot of being a doctor is rounds and paperwork – make sure you see some of this as well, to decide if you can also see yourself doing these parts of the job.

Not being assertive can lead to you missing out on good opportunities to talk to patients, ask questions and maybe even see some interesting procedures. Be confident and let the people that you are working with know what you would like to get out of your work experience placement. But remember, this should not come off as you being rude, arrogant or careless about their work load.

Ensure that you do not do things (even is doctor allows you to) that you are not qualified to do. Although it may not seem like this would not happen, unfortunately it does, and far too often. It may not feel like a problem if the doctor allows you to, but remember that one of the biggest values of being a doctor is ensuring that you do no harm, and by doing something that you are not qualified to do could put you in a position to do harm.

THE IMPORTANCE OF WORK EXPERIENCE

WHAT DO THE UNIVERSITIES SAY?

Universities are in agreement that medical work experience allows you to get the best understanding of medicine as a career, to enable you to make a well-educated decision. Medical schools will assess your work experience in a variety of ways to ensure that you were involved in your placement and that you are able to learn in a hands-on learning environment.

Their assessment of your work experience will be through your personal statement, perhaps at your interview. Some universities will also ask that you provide details of your medical work experience separate to your UCAS application.

Some medical schools score the personal statements that they receive. However, most use them to verify that their applicants have the relevant and required work experience, and to see what it is that has been gained from their work experience placements.

Most universities will discuss your work experience during the interview, either by asking questions that are specific to you and your work experience opportunities (more often in panel-style interviews) or by asking general questions regarding work experience and what you were able to learn (more often in MMI-style interviews).

Universities tend to require you to have done medical work experience if you want to apply to medical school because they want to know that you have done some preparation and put in effort to broaden your understanding of what a career in medicine is comprised of. This is because universities spend a lot of time and money on each medical student that they accept onto their course, and so they want to be reasonably confident in their decision to accept you. By taking part in medical work experience and showing that you can get involved and want to learn from the opportunities available to you, you are already demonstrating your commitment to medicine and your understanding of what is expected of you now and in the future. This makes you a more desirable candidate for medical schools to take a risk on, as you are more prepared to complete the degree and to complete it well.

Medical schools commonly suggest that work experience should allow you to obtain a realistic insight of all the aspects of becoming and being a healthcare professional. This includes the essential values required to be a good doctor, and the emotional and physical demands of working in healthcare – where the focus is always patient-centred. The way in which you manage to gain this understanding (regardless of the specific environment) will be deemed appropriate by the universities. However, universities strongly recommend that prospective students engage with a caring role – whether voluntary, paid or observational – as a part of their work experience.

In general, medical schools do not encourage medical work experience to be done abroad. This is mainly because UK medical schools are looking for students that understand the health system in the UK and want to work in the UK. However, overseas work experience could be an amazing opportunity given that it is justifiable, and that it is a financially responsible decision on your part. This may be more of a consideration for prospective students whose home country is abroad or if they are an overseas applicant. It is worth noting that if you are applying from outside of the UK, you are not required to travel to the UK to complete work experience within the UK health system. As previously mentioned (see "Where should I do my work experience?" on page 13), there are other ways to learn about what medicine is like and what you should expect while you study, and one day practice, medicine.

"You have developed some of the values, attitudes and behaviours essential to being a doctor such as conscientiousness, good communication skills, and the ability to interact with a wide variety of people. The values that medical schools are looking for are set out in the NHS Constitution and explained in the MSC guidance Core values and aptitudes needed to study medicine."

(Guidance on relevant experience for applying to medical school, 2017)

WHAT DO THE PROFESSIONAL BODIES SAY?

In general, the requirement is that you have engaged with people-focused work experiences, during which you have observed and been involved in providing care for others. This is in an effort to ensure that you have gained a realistic understanding of the degree that you are applying for and of what it is like to have a career in a caring profession.

The General Medical Council (GMC) works in the UK to protect the patients, improve the medical education and standardise the clinical practice in the UK by regulating and setting the standards for healthcare professionals.

The GMC: "Students can gain practical experience and find out more about a career in medicine through work observation."

(Work experience and doctors in training, 2021)

The British Medical Association (BMA) is a trade union for doctors within the UK. Although BMA does not certify doctors or regulate their practice – as this is the GMC's responsibility –, they do represent doctors and medical students, while working towards outstanding healthcare.

The BMA: "All UK medical schools now require applicants to have experience in a caring or service role, either paid or voluntarily, in health or related field, as well as direct observation healthcare."

(Getting medical work experience, 2021)

Professional bodies operating in the UK agree that medical work experience allows for prospective students to show their enthusiasm for their future career, whilst developing key skills that are required by both medical students and doctors in practice. The sooner that these skills are developed and refined, the better for engaging with learning, effectively practicing medicine and interacting with patients and colleagues. It is good to be prepared to demonstrate these skills in your application and during your interview.

WHAT DO THE HOSPITALS SAY?

The hospitals in the UK are generally a part of the NHS (National Health Service) healthcare system. The NHS was founded on a set of seven key values and principles, which is referred to as the NHS Constitution.

Hospitals require that universities choose individuals that have the potential to serve these values well, and that they teach and facilitate the development of their medical students to embody these values in learning and practice.

In general, most hospitals have schemes in place that allow individuals that want to do work experience to do so in a controlled and regulated manner. There are often some rules regarding the required age, length of work experience placement, departments that are available for shadowing, etc. But the hospitals are often very friendly and would love to welcome prospective medical students into a few days in the life of a healthcare professional.

WHAT DO SUCCESSFUL APPLICANTS SAY?

Successful applicants are generally very positive about their time doing work experience and report having gained so much from their placements – from insight into medicine, to essential attributes of a medical student, to even potentially having found a future specialty to pursue and train in.

The main takeaway that most individuals have from their work experience is that they now have a much more realistic idea about what medicine involves as a degree and as a career. Many say that they had misconceptions about medicine because they applied what they knew about being a patient to what they assumed being a doctor would be like. But now, they feel like they are equipped to make a decision about whether they are well-suited to medicine, whether they will thrive in this career and whether they can commit to five plus years of studying followed by many years of training and specialisation.

"It made me realise how diverse the field of medicine truly is. My placement was mostly in surgery but I also saw the work of nurses, admin staff, neurologists and radiologists and was able to sit in on clinics, which helped me appreciate the range of opportunities I will have when I become a doctor myself."

"It exposed me to the realities of working in medicine from the professional's perspective for the first time. Medicine isn't all about medication and surgeries, it's also about treating the patient holistically and taking into account many of the social aspects that contribute to a patient's health and wellbeing."

Many also say that their perception of what it is that doctors and other healthcare professionals do each day at work has been radically changed. Some say for the better because they would prefer to become a doctor now that they have this insight, and some for the worse, but that they now know that medicine is not the career for them.

"My work experience confirmed my decision to study medicine, but it did also change my perception. It made me realise that doctors' work is far less glamorous than is portrayed in TV and media, with much of their days being taken up by paperwork. But it made me realise the importance of social interaction and personal skills, and how much I value this in my future profession. This is one of the reasons I decided to follow a career in medicine."

Some say that their work experience helped to set straight some of the false judgements that they had. Many were interested in pursuing medicine, but holding themselves back because of something someone had told them, or something they had read, or just due to uncertainty about whether they are the 'right type of person'. By shadowing healthcare professionals, talking to patients and asking doctors questions, these uncertainties were able to be addressed.

"This was the first time I had a serious chat with many people, from different fields and levels of the profession, about what the career was like on a personal and emotional basis."

"I was somewhat worried about medicine being so intense that I would not be able to enjoy my work, but the placement showed me that intensity does not necessarily mean that the job will not also be fun!"

In hindsight, students that have completed their work experience in many different areas with many different people fully support their decision to do so. It is more varied and less monotonous, plus you have a much better chance of experiencing something that you truly enjoy and can become passionate about as you approach medical school.

"Try and get as much varied experience and insight as you can, as it will help you go into the application process and the career with your eyes wide open and could help inspire you, or even reveal that you may not want to commit years of your life in pursuit of this."

Whether you have personal experience of medicine – for example by having doctors in your family – or not, work experience will allow you to form your own opinions about the career that you are considering embarking on. Although other peoples' experiences are very valuable, some aspects need to be experienced and understood personally.

"Coming from a non-medical family, I definitely had a very idealised view of the profession. Work experience was a wake-up call for me as to what medicine is really like: rewarding, yet at times demanding and stressful. I realised that medicine is not just a career, but a lifelong commitment to learning and developing your knowledge to benefit your patients. Use your work experience to properly decide that this is something you want to do."

All in all, most individuals that have completed medical work experience will tell you that it was very eye-opening and that it no doubt had a massive impact on how they understand and approach medicine; that was a useful experience that taught individuals a lot about themselves and developed character traits that will be useful in life no matter what.

"It gave me a newfound appreciation for the medical profession, and I will take that with me wherever I go in my life. Everyone and anyone who is lucky enough to undertake a medical work experience placement should do so."

WHAT DO DOCTORS SAY?

Doctors have expressed that medical work experience prior to medical school is hugely important and incredibly valuable. Many doctors look back on the contributing factors to what lead them to pursue medicine (and potentially even their specialty), and many pinpoint that their interest was cemented into a decision during their work experience:

"Prior to my placement I wasn't sure exactly what I was going to study. In fact, I even had a separate placement a few weeks earlier in a trading floor at a London bank. The two placements couldn't have been more different. However, even though the doctors I met were extremely busy and often on their feet the whole day, the work had a buzz to it that I was hooked on. I found the science challenging yet interesting and thought provoking, I found the communication demanding yet fulfilling, and on the whole, I found my placement enjoyable.

Even now, working as a junior, there are days that are very challenging but I still enjoy a huge number of my days at work and am very glad that the placement pointed me in this direction."

Whether your medical work experience plants seeds of interest in the medical profession where there were none before (as per the personal experience on the previous page) or whether it waters the seeds that have been previously planted, it will have an effect on what you pursue and how you decide to pursue that.

Doctors, on the whole, regard their medical work experience prior to their medical school applications very fondly and overflowing with experiences that moulded their career and specialty to this day. So make sure that you take your work experience seriously, and that you enable yourself to explore all of your options!

BUT WHY?

MAKING AN INFORMED DECISION

Medicine is a lifelong commitment. It is a long degree and an even longer career. You want to prepare yourself to make this decision as best as you can with the information you have available to you – and through medical work experience, you will have a lot more information available to you.

Medical work experience (and your learning points stemming from your work experience) show that you understand what a career in medicine involves, while allowing you to accumulate and develop the traits and skills that are needed by doctors. A very important aspect that is worth getting your head around early (work experience may be the best time for this!) is your own abilities, and even more importantly, your own limitations within the context of a healthcare setting.

A career in medicine is unique in that it combines teamwork with individual knowledge, and patient-centred care by communicating well with many others. Working in a multi-disciplinary team is a key component of any specialty in medicine, and so, experiencing this and understanding how they operate will help you decide if this is a way that you could enjoy working. Plus, perhaps the most important aspect that you need to consider is whether you feel comfortable and enjoy working in a healthcare environment; this is the one certainty that will be a vital component of whichever direction or specialty you choose to pursue.

Medicine is a hugely challenging career that will force you to deal with situations that you never would have imagined, that will teach you how to grow and that will humble you each and every day. A very important part of work experience – and your time during medical school and beyond – is being able to identify your own strengths and weaknesses. One of the best ways to gain this type of insight about yourself is to ask your colleagues and teachers about your learning-style and rapport with patients. While it may seem like beginning to discuss this during work experience is a little premature, the healthcare professionals that you will be shadowing will have had this 'learning conversation' many times before, and they can give you some great pointers!

"Benefits of the experience are that it gave me my most realistic introduction yet into the medical world. Although I came from a medical background, it was my work experience that gave me an idea of what the job involved. One of the most valuable learning points was taking away a realistic understanding of what the profession involves, which consisted of getting lots of peoples' views and building my own perceptions based on what you observed. This is a decision that others can help support in, but it is for you and you alone to make."

UNDERSTANDING THE CAREER

Medical work experience is great to get anywhere in your local area that relates to healthcare or people-centred service. Often this will be in the form of volunteering, for example this could be at care homes, hospices, general practice surgeries or hospitals.

Other ways that are useful to help build your understanding of the career is to engage with activities that are focused on delivery of healthcare, or on education regarding medicine. These may include following medical journals, reading books written by healthcare professionals, or keeping up with news about the NHS.

Even if you are able to secure work experience placements, I strongly recommend that you also build on your knowledge about the career you are applying to pursue by engaging with available material in the above outlined ways. These activities will emphasise your interest in a medical degree and career, as well as your willingness to do individual research and further your own personal interests.

"Arranging time to speak with professionals will provide you with material to use in your interview, as well as demonstrate your motivation and initiative. Everyone you meet can be valuable sources of information and experience; don't focus on just the doctors."

If you know any doctors or healthcare professionals – whether current or retired – try to arrange time to meet with them to talk about their jobs and experiences. Anyone that has any experience in the healthcare sector would be able to give you some worthwhile points and interesting insights into what they have seen, done and been a part of. If you have the opportunities to, speak to people that are perhaps slightly removed from the 'frontline' of medicine (i.e. make sure that you don't just focus on doctors and other healthcare professionals), but speak to people involved in research, policies, ethics, law – whoever you can manage to make contact with! They will all no doubt be able to give you some great insight and suggestions regarding your time at medical school, as a junior doctor, while specialising and well into your future in medicine.

"This was the first time I had a serious chat with many people, from different fields and levels of the profession, about what the career was like on a personal and emotional basis. I don't think I properly understood the variety of work that doctors carry out, it is a lot more than just treating patients. I realised that the job required constant learning to keep on top of the field, and about the importance of organisation as there is a lot of paperwork behind the scenes."

COMMITMENT TO THE CAREER

It is difficult to commit to a lifelong career without being confident in your understanding of what said career entails. Similarly, as an individual who is not yet in medical school –and therefore not yet involved in pursuing a career in medicine – it is difficult to break through into the medical world and gain this understanding. However, you can put additional efforts towards less 'hands-on' and 'mainstream' activities that fewer people tend to engage with. This will help you to show your unique commitment to medicine.

"Every prospective medical student is doing work experience because they are considering becoming a doctor. But it is important to demonstrate that you have thought about this decision, and do not have an idealistic view of a career in medicine."

You want to demonstrate that you have an accurate view of what being a doctor is like, and that it is *still* the right choice for you, and you are confident that you have what it takes to be a good doctor. Your commitment to the degree and your passion for the career is what universities want to see in the students that they accept into their medical school. They want to be confident in your confidence to study medicine, and be sure that you will see it through and enjoy it too!

41

GAINING TRANSFERABLE SKILLS

"You have developed some of the values, attitudes and behaviours essential to being a doctor such as conscientiousness, good communication skills, and the ability to interact with a wide variety of people."

(Guidance on relevant experience for applying to medical school, 2017)

Conscientiousness, good communication and effective interaction with a variety of people are important skills that have been highlighted – among others – as skills that you should seek to acquire and refine during your medical work experience.

As aforementioned (see "Making an informed decision" on page 37), you may think that it seems to be a little soon to be gaining and working on skills that you will need to use throughout your training and practice as a doctor. However, recognising the importance of these skills and having an understanding of them, will help to make your medical school experience smoother and set you ahead of your peers early on in the process.

Other important skills to consider and observe in the professionals you are shadowing include respect, teamwork, collaboration, resilience and empathy.

"Autonomy, respect and confidentiality are hugely important in clinical professions that are often public-facing, and therefore it is crucial that you acquire these traits in training. It may feel out of the comfort zone for some, which is natural, but people rarely learn or grow in the comfort zone, and this exposure early on can be built on in future placements."

Be sure to focus on the way that the professionals you are shadowing interact with one another. As a doctor, you will not be working on your own, but always as part of a much larger team. You will need to be able to work well in a team to deliver effective care to patients, and enjoy yourself while doing so. Take note of the collaboration, communication and respect that the doctors exhibit while working with one another, but even more so, while working in the context of the multidisciplinary team – which is more often than not.

"It [my work experience] highlighted that being a doctor involves lots of collaboration with healthcare professionals, so teamwork and communication is key."

Your character and skills as a doctor will have the power to change your patients' experiences as they are treated by you and your team. Patients' experiences in hospital are often scary and filled with uncertainty, which makes many (understandably) feel very vulnerable at times under our care. Don't underestimate the effect that our interactions can have on others – a good doctor can treat and care for the *whole* person, not just their diagnosis.

WHY WORK EXPERIENCE?

"Observing emotionally difficult conversations between doctors and patients allowed me to appreciate the difference that rapport and empathy can make to how a patient feels about their encounter with a healthcare professional, and subsequently, how they view their care and treatment plan."

DEVELOPMENT AS A PERSON/STUDENT

Medicine is widely regarded as a degree and career that undoubtedly facilitates the development of one's skills and character, in ways that will also overflow into one's daily life. Working in healthcare is unlike many other professions, because you are caring for vulnerable individuals, often during uncertain and life-changing situations.

"In every job, you will have difficult days, but it's important that you focus on the positive aspects of the job and know you are making a real difference. You must remember that for many patients, it is their quality of life that is more important than their quantity of life."

What draws many individuals to medicine as a career is that it will inevitably involve constant learning due to the evolving nature of science and medicine. Change and continuous development is a part of the job title, so it should not come as a surprise that you should expect to begin learning already during your work experience placements.

"The best way to learn something is to do it."

DEMONSTRATING YOUR INTEREST AND VALUES

The work experience placements that you secure, and the extracurricular activities that you partake in, allow you to demonstrate your personal interests and values. Use this opportunity to set yourself apart in the eyes of the university admissions team who will be reading your personal statement as well as the people who will be interviewing you.

Allow your personal interests and values to become a part of who you are, also while you are in the work place, or in other words, during your work experience. It is worth mentioning that this is within reason obviously, and you should not express views that some may find offensive or force any opinions on anyone.

The people that you shadow and work with during your medical work experience may have the same interests as you or just take interest in what you have expressed. The people you meet and get along with could be useful to know – for the duration of your work experience, but even more so for your future within the medical profession.

The way that you carry yourself and interact with others will open doors for you, if you need help or advice from the people that you meet and build rapport with. Your medical work experience is a great opportunity to begin creating a network of contacts that could help you in the future – whether this is for further work experience opportunities, during medical school or even as a practicing doctor.

ABILITY TO WORK/INTERACT WITH OTHERS (IN A TEAM)

Being able to work with a wide range of people with different backgrounds and different opinions is a very important part of any career in which a service is being provided. Not only is this true for your interactions with your patients, but also regarding your interactions with your colleagues. Your colleagues are the team of people that you will spend a significant proportion of your time with in a day, and they may be the difference between enjoying your work and 'just getting through the work day'.

"Prior to work experience I had believed that the role of a doctor was much more independent than it is. By observing doctors relying on the cooperation of other members of the healthcare team, I realised the importance of a cohesive, multi-disciplinary approach to patient care."

Your ability do work with others well – and interact with your colleagues and patients effectively – is a vital part of providing good care to your patients. It is never too early to begin considering how it is that you work in team, and what aspects of your team-working may require some work. Having this self-awareness – or at least being able to take on and implement constructive criticism – will stand you in good stead as you go through the application process, and as you take on medical school.

"I found my experience very informative and insightful. Prior to having work experience, I was unaware of the multifaceted nature of medicine. After all, doctors work as part of large teams involving many healthcare professionals, so demonstrating that you have a sense of those professions and how they work together will help you in both your personal statement and interview."

Teamwork is what makes a career in medicine collaborative and allows for better holistic patient care, rather than individually-driven care based purely on scientific facts. Teamwork is such a vital part of clinical medicine; it is often mentioned by doctors as one of the aspects that helps them get through the difficulties of working as a doctor and makes their work fun. A very important point to consider before committing to medicine, is whether you thrive working on your own (maybe consider a less collaborative career) or whether you work well and enjoy working in a team (maybe continue to pursue a career in medicine).

TYPES OF WORK EXPERIENCE

OVERVIEW

There are many different ways that you can go about getting work experience. There are some guidelines regarding university's preferences for work experience – including the type, time, duration and learning points (see the outlines given in 'The Basics' from page 9).

As there are so many different options for how you can go about gaining medical work experience, it makes sense that you would pursue opportunities that you are interested in (so that you enjoy the placement) and that may facilitate you to move out of your comfort zone (so that you maximise what you are able to learn from it).

As a general rule, it is a good idea to have a variety of medical work experience placements to ensure you have the opportunity to see different healthcare environments and can gain a broad understanding. The main opportunities that you should endeavour to plan include shadowing based in a department in a hospital setting, shadowing in a community setting (commonly in a GP surgery) and volunteering.

The volunteering opportunity would preferably be a long-term commitment, which would allow you to build relationships and observe care being followed through. Some applicant's best experiences and talking points for interviews stem from their volunteering.

"There are many options for work experience that is relevant to medicine, and if possible, try and undertake a few different kinds. The most obvious options are shadowing doctors and other health professionals at a hospital or GP surgery, which will give you an idea of what a doctor's day looks like. Voluntary work, such as in a care home or hospital, is another great option, and many medical schools will look for this in addition to shadowing, as volunteering over an extended time both shows your commitment, and that you have experienced working in caring environment."

HOSPITAL-BASED PLACEMENTS

Hospital-based placements are the setting and type that most people think about when they think about medical work experience. These placements may be the best opportunities to experience what your life as a practicing doctor may be, while also allowing you to interact with other healthcare professionals within the context of a multidisciplinary team.

Medical work experience placements in hospital departments gives you the opportunity to choose which specialties you may want to experience in the run up to your applications. This could be in line with interests that you already have, or specialties that you think you would enjoy doing your work experience in.

Hospital-based placements tend to be organised through medical work experience schemes run by the hospitals, and so they are often more structured, with the healthcare professionals that you will be shadowing often having plenty of previous experience with prospective medical students completing work experience with them and their team.

Some individuals find hospital-based medical work experience opportunities difficult to find, and unfortunately, depending on your local hospitals, this may be quite common. However, don't be easily discouraged if this is the case, because persistence will give you the best shot at securing an opportunity, and if not, then draw on what you learnt from *this* experience anyway!

Hospital-based work experience tends to be shorter than community-based placements or volunteering opportunities. Commonly, you will spend about a week gaining work experience in one department. This may seem like a very short time to understand the specialty and to understand what to expect from a career in medicine, but keep in mind that you will most likely be there from 8-4 or 9-5 each day, and most days will be very similar in terms of what you are able to observe on work experience.

In most departments, your day will begin with a ward round of either all the patients on the ward or just the patients who have been newly admitted the day or night before. This is an excellent opportunity to be a part of as you will get to listen to the multidisciplinary team discuss many different patients and their conditions, as well as their treatment plans and what the team's hopes are for their recovery. After rounds, what happens is largely dependent on the ward and department, however, often the more junior doctors will have a list of 'jobs' to work on throughout the day, while the more senior doctors will have surgeries or run clinics. I would suggest you split the days that you have between the different opportunities presented to you for the individuals you can shadow and the activities you can take part in.

The way that each day goes will also depend on whether you are doing your work experience on a medical or surgical ward. Surgical wards tend to be more fast-paced, with patients being prepared for and recovering from surgery. The patients also tend to be more ill on surgical wards compared to medical wards; this means that you may not be able to talk to as many patients as you potentially could speak to on medical wards, where patients tend to stay for longer periods and usually very happy to chat to new faces.

"My first hospital experience was in the summer of Year 11, and it was a very eye-opening experience that revealed the harsh realities of being a doctor. The monotony of every day working life was seen in junior doctors, as well as the relationships within the hierarchical system of the various ranks of doctors. It was incredibly interesting if you have a doctor who is open to talking to you about things alongside their work (which is understandably very difficult!). You get to really see how busy doctors, nurses and other medical staff are, and how hard they work. If you have a passion for this subject and career, I think these parts of the job don't seem like they are such big deals, especially if you expect it now that you have done work experience. You need to really want to do medicine and be a doctor to enjoy the journey and the job."

COMMUNITY-BASED PLACEMENTS

Community-based placements are a great place to gain experience on work experience opportunities that are more long-term. Working in medicine does not only involve hospital-based work, but often also involves working in the community. Whether this is because of the specialty you choose to train in, or because this is one of the rotations you are assigned to during your foundation doctor training.

When students consider medical work experience, there is a tendency to immediately think about the aforementioned 'hospital-based placements' (see page 49) as the only 'real' option to pursue for your medical work experience. However, universities and hospitals agree that for potential medical students to gain a good and realistic understanding of this career, they just need to observe professionals in their day-to-day lives and gain some experience with interacting with patients. Fulfilling these criteria is often actually easier and more enjoyable in a community-based placement, rather than a very busy, high-pressure hospital environment.

"Universities say that it does not have to be a flashy placement and can be something as simple as chatting to patients in a care home whilst volunteering and seeing community-based care. The emphasis is really on the reflection of the experience."

Work experience opportunities in the community tend to be more accessible, and often students report that they enjoyed this placement more than they did the hospital-based placement because they were able to get more involved. As a prospective student undertaking medical work experience with no medical training yet, what you are able to do on your hospital placements with acutely unwell patients will be very limited. Whereas in the community, you tend to work with older individuals or individuals that are more chronically ill (physically or mentally). So there is more opportunity to gain an understanding of the patient experience, to learn about the patients' different conditions as well as to potentially even get involved in patient service and care (depending on the individual establishment, the nature of the service/care and given that you are being sufficiently supervised).

"My experience mainly involved spending time and doing activities with people living in a residential home, many of whom had quite severe disabilities. It was definitely challenging at times, but ended up being incredibly rewarding, and helped me develop skills which were not only useful in interviews, but also for patient interactions as a medical student."

Medical schools really like to see long-term community-based work experience placements in their applicants' personal statements. It shows that you are able to commit to a caring role in the long-term and that you value this opportunity to gain this experience and develop these skills. You are also showing the medical school that you don't mind putting in extra work, and that you are doing your best to prepare yourself to study medicine and to do it well. These are all valuable character traits to have as a prospective medical student, you want to highlight them to the medical school admissions team in your application for medicine.

"Although my hospital placement was inspiring and made me excited at the prospect of becoming a doctor, a week is not long enough to absorb all there is to learn. The placement which really opened my eyes to the realities of medicine was at a hospice. I volunteered for 18 months during sixth form and it was invaluable. My role included keeping patients company and making cups of tea for family and friends. Although I never did anything 'directly' medical, I learnt to communicate effectively and how to remain composed in difficult situations: skills I now use daily as a medical student."

VOLUNTEERING

Volunteering is also a great way to gain medical work experience. Similar to the aforementioned points (see "Community-based placements" on page 52), volunteering also tends to be longer-term. This gives you the opportunity to show the medical admissions teams that you are a hardworking student who values the chance to work in a caring role, and who will therefore have a well-informed understanding of what to expect when training and practicing as a doctor.

"Volunteering at a care home is a great way to improve your empathy and compassion whilst helping out in a much-needed sector and improving the quality of life of often socially isolated elderly people. Furthermore, care homes are often much easier to get a volunteering post at than hospitals."

It is an especially good idea to consider a long-term volunteering opportunities if you find that you are struggling to secure a work experience placement in a hospital or the community. Universities acknowledge that it may be difficult to find such placements, and in that case, taking initiative to gain some of the experience and develop the necessary skills in another manner is commendable.

"If you genuinely cannot find any clinically-based work experience, medical schools do understand this and often value volunteering regularly in a clinical setting, such as a care home as equally valuable, with much of what you learn being very similar."

Working with people who are older, disabled or disadvantaged is the best place to start looking for volunteering opportunities. This will provide you with an idea of what the medical world is like while giving you the chance to develop skills that can be applied to training and working as a doctor. However, volunteering in any capacity can be used to support your suitability to study medicine, and it will allow you to develop your character and gain new skills, while helping people that need your support.

"Voluntary work, such as in a care home or hospital, is a great option, and many medical schools will look for this in addition to shadowing. Volunteering over an extended time shows your commitment, and that you have experienced working in caring environment."

SHADOWING THE MULTIDISCIPLINARY TEAM

As a medical student and a doctor, you are working as a part of a much larger team to provide care to individuals when they are most vulnerable. To provide effective care, it is very important to work well as a team, and to respect the contributions that each member of the team makes. The first step in this respect is understanding what it is that each professional does. Plus, it is always good to know what you can expect each professional to do and be in charge of so that you're not running in circles trying to follow up tests and consultations from the wrong people or teams.

"I got the opportunity to shadow not just the GP, but a wide range of other healthcare professionals such as a nurse practitioner, an osteopath, and a drugs and alcohol nurse. As a medic you will eventually be working in a multi-disciplinary team, so it is helpful to know about the variety of roles available. This will also be useful when it comes to discussing your teamwork knowledge in an interview setting."

An understanding of what working in the context of a multi-disciplinary team involves is a very worthwhile learning point to take from your work experience, as this will be an integral part of each day while being a medical student on the wards and while working as a doctor in whichever environment that may be. In medicine, you don't work as an individual, but rather as a team, and so you need to be able to exhibit these traits and explain your understanding thereof during your medical school interviews.

During your work experience in the clinical setting, make an effort to shadow the other professionals that are a part of the multidisciplinary team. This can be organised by specifically asking the administrative team in charge of your work experience to arrange this for you. Alternatively, you could take advantage of the time when your team of doctors are busy or writing up reports, and approach the other professionals on your ward to ask if you could shadow them for a couple hours. Some people that you may want to consider shadowing include nurses, nursing assistants (NAs)/ healthcare assistants (HCAs), pharmacists, physiotherapists, occupational therapists, dieticians, speech and language therapists, and many more.

"When my cardiologist was busy, I had the opportunity to shadow a specialist cardiac nurse and ask her questions about her job too. If you do have time during your work experience, ask to shadow different healthcare professionals in order to get a more holistic and multidisciplinary viewpoint of medical care."

Don't underestimate the value of pursuing work experience opportunities that you assume are not directly related to medicine. For example, you could think about organising a couple days or weeks of work experience with a laboratory, pharmacy, chiropractor, osteopath, physiotherapist, nursery, school, day-care, and many more. There is so much to learn from the other professionals and departments that are providing care to other individuals – whether this is similar or different to what you anticipate in medicine. Even if what you observe while shadowing others is not what you expect to need to do when you are a practicing doctor, you will still observe patient-facing care, develop skills needed to work in a caring profession and grow your network of contacts that may be useful to have in the future.

"Obvious places to gain medical work experience are hospitals and surgeries, but you can also try pharmacies, care homes, mental health clinics, chiropractors, physiotherapists, nurseries, schools, etc. Anywhere you can think of that is involved in the wider NHS umbrella, or that involves caring for people in some capacity, can be useful work experience. You could also look at getting work experience from a lab if you are at all interested in research or you are looking to apply to a science-heavy course."

Also don't forget to ask the other professionals that you shadow questions about their job and even questions that you have about training and practicing as a doctor. They may have very interesting and insightful opinions and information from an 'outsider's view' – so don't discount their answers and experience based on the fact that they aren't doctors.

WORK EXPERIENCE IN DEPRIVED AREAS

The impact of socio-economic factors on individuals' health is an important concept for medical students and doctors to understand and consider. The location of the GP surgery or hospital that you work at will have a direct impact on the demographics of the patients that you will be treating. This will have a knock-on effect on the conditions that tend to present and the primary health concerns that individuals tend to have.

"The fact the practice was in a deprived area allowed me to see first-hand the many socio-economic factors that contribute to health, which is an area I believe it is important for all prospective medical students to be aware of."

This is relevant for areas that are more urban versus rural; for areas that are more affluent versus deprived; for areas that are nearer holiday destinations versus residential areas. If you have the means and/or opportunity to do so, consider these aspects as you are organising and even carrying out your work experience placements.

There are a few things to keep in mind for working in surgeries or hospitals in areas that a more deprived. Although these are considerations that you should ideally have regardless of where you are doing your placement, it is really important for your safety and wellbeing that you do consider and plan for them prior to beginning your placement in more deprived areas. A few examples of such considerations include: how to interact with patients effectively, which conditions and/or presentations are more common, which procedures are done more often, what your plans for lunch are, how you are going to travel to and from placement each day, and which contacts do you have nearby.

WORK EXPERIENCE OUTSIDE OF THE UK

Undertaking medical work experience outside of the UK is a great opportunity, however, it is by no means necessary or advantageous to have for your application. Doing anything abroad obviously requires you the means to do so, and this is something that universities know and appreciate, and obviously do not insist on. So, don't worry if you haven't done or aren't planning to do any work experience abroad, because it will not – in any way – make you a less desirable candidate in comparison to those who have.

Some of the reasons that individuals do part of their work experience abroad is they want to experience healthcare in different places, they want to volunteer in developing countries, or they are considering practicing abroad one day and want to get a taster for what this may involve. All of these (and more) are very valid reasons for doing your work experience abroad. Just remember, it is not about where you did your work experience (whether this is which country, which establishment or which department), but rather all about what you learnt from your time of work experience.

Doing some medical work experience abroad is a great opportunity to learn about disparities in healthcare. You can gain understanding that the prevalence of disease is different depending on the area, broaden your knowledge of a career in medicine, and experience the dynamics of how different teams work together, while allowing you to spend some time exploring new places. However, you can learn most of this by doing some research, without needing to spend extra money.

"I wanted work experience in a different country, especially a developing country, in order to compare medical care and treatment given to patients, and to enhance my knowledge and understanding of medical practices where resources are scarcer."

60

It is worth keeping in mind, that as you are applying to a UK medical school, you should be doing at least part of your medical work experience in the UK and ideally, within the National Health Service. It is quite difficult to persuade admissions tutors and interviewers that you are passionate about studying in and working for the NHS if you haven't experienced it from a 'working perspective' and haven't really made an effort to do so either.

Another consideration is that you may be under the age of 18 at the time of your work experience if you are doing it during your years at school, so going abroad may not be an option unless you have family or friends that can go with you or who live in your destination country and could act as your guardians for the duration of your placement. One way that individuals manage to get experience abroad is through paid opportunities with companies and work experience schemes (see "Paid 'work experience' and 'educational experiences'" on page 67 for more information on this topic), however, given the costs associated this is definitely not required.

There are many different ways to go about planning medical work experience in a different country. One of the most successful ways is to do so through contacts that you have in the country – whether they are medically involved or not. You will most likely require a short CV outlining all the basic information about you that you think would 'sell' you as a work experience candidate, and a letter in which you describe why you want to undertake work experience in that country, what makes you a good candidate to do so and what you hope to achieve during this work experience. (See "Writing a CV" on page 131 for more information on this topic).

"I made sure that my CV included my interests in volunteering in developing countries throughout my career, and how I would benefit from learning about health conditions that were more typical in the developing countries than the UK! I made sure to include that I could speak the local language, as I knew I would need it at the rural hospital. In my covering letter, I mentioned my interest in tropical health conditions and how exciting it would be to learn about the management of these conditions as they were not in my curriculum."

You will need to contact the director or individual in charge of student experiences at the hospital you want to be placed at with your CV, the dates you propose, your intended goals/outcomes, your potential interests and any other information that they may require from you. You may be asked to fill in a form, attach evidence of your education history, give permission from your parents/guardians, etc.

"I would contact friends/relatives in a country that you would like to do work experience in, and tell them about your requirements and what field you would be interested in, and then email the

superintendent/director of a local hospital, for their approval for work experience."

If you have the time and the means (mainly contacts, finances and time), then doing some medical work experience abroad can be a great opportunity – for your application and for your own individual development. Be prepared for it to be different – and most likely more difficult – than your placements in the UK, both in terms of organising them and carrying them out. However, with careful planning and organisation, you will hopefully have a great experience of medicine in a different country, and you will definitely reap the benefits of stepping out of your comfort zone!

The following is the experience of a current medical student who completed her second work experience placement in South Africa during a family holiday, after really enjoying the medical environment in her first placement and wanting to experience this in a different country:

"I did a week of work experience abroad during a family holiday to South Africa. Everyone was really friendly and happy to have a 'foreign student' on the wards. The local hospital challenged my perception of healthcare there, as I imagined it would be much less developed based on the media's portrayal of it. I really enjoyed chatting to the patients about their lives and learning more about South Africa too, plus it made my holiday feel a bit productive.

I would strongly recommend to do even just a few days in a different country (on a family holiday, for example), just to experience how incredibly different the same medical care can 'feel'. Make sure you plan for it well, and you anticipate any potential problems you could face."

INTERNSHIPS

Internships are not particularly common in terms of gaining medical work experience. This is mainly due to the nature of internships (i.e. the more corporate nature), and that often the outcome of internships may be an entry-level job offer, which is obviously not possible in medicine until you have completed the required medicine degree.

Some people may decide to pursue internships in medically-related areas, and even take on part-time (alongside school or studies) or full-time (usually during gap years) jobs in these areas. For example, these may include working as an assistant, as a scribe, as a secretary, in data analysis/input work and many more.

As you may be able to tell, most of these jobs are more admin-related than being medically- or clinically-related. However, there is lots to learn in terms of personal development, communication skills and teamworking from these types of internships. There is also the added benefit of working in a clinical environment, and so you will automatically be 'in the loop' because you are interested in what is going on around you, and even more so if you express interest in studying medicine one day. Additionally, the people you work with could no doubt be important and useful contacts to have both now and in the future. So, don't underestimate the people who are not doctors just because they aren't doctors and you want to become a doctor.

64

PART-TIME JOBS

Part-time jobs are a great way to get stuck into the 'medical world'. Often, these jobs are less clinically-related, and more based on administrative jobs. But although this may seem counterintuitive and not particularly helpful for you to gain medical work experience, it is a great place to start.

Part-time jobs allow you to get a feeling for the working environment from a less pressure-heavy position. This will also allow you to form part of your opinion from the 'outside-in', perhaps before you get too close to the medical profession itself. There is the obvious benefit of earning some money by working part-time, but also that you will be given the opportunity to develop interpersonal skills that will be so valuable in whichever career direction you pursue.

Working as a healthcare assistant (also referred to as a nursing assistant) is a great part-time job, which is an opportunity to gain great experience and is also clinically relevant. HCAs work with nurses to assist in clinical duties, patients' personal care and supporting to improve patient care. This is a very challenging – but rewarding – job that is often flexible, especially if working as a part of the bank staff.

"I worked as an HCA on the weekends during my last school year. It was an enriching experience that cemented by decision to pursue medicine, while allowing me to work in healthcare now."

OPEN DAYS

University open days give you the opportunity to learn more about the course and the specific universities that you are considering applying to. Although medicine is a relatively standardised course within the UK, there are still quite big differences in the methods that certain medical schools use to teach, in the content/clinical experience that certain medical schools follow and in the opportunities available to learn from offered by different medical schools.

Make sure that you take the time to learn about all the different components on the medicine courses that you are interested in, and that you know what you can expect from each university. This is a hugely important part for your interviews too. Most universities will include a question (whether panel- or MMI-style) regarding their unique teaching and learning opportunities or they may ask you what draws you to their course specifically. This is the perfect opportunity to show that you have done your research and that you know more about the course that you interviewing for than just that it is medicine and you want to be a doctor.

Use in-person open days to also explore the campus; most medical schools are off-site, so make sure that you find out where your teaching will take place and you will be spending your time. Make sure you also ask any questions that you have (whether the open day is in-person or online), as this is the best opportunity you will have to get answers from individuals that are well-informed and happy to help.

COMPETITIONS AND CHALLENGES

Competitions and challenges aren't really considered work experience as such, but they are good opportunities to get involved with medically-related tasks and experiences. This also gives you another aspect of your exploration of a medical career to discuss in your personal statement and during your interviews.

Some ideas to begin thinking about could be to take part in writing challenges – some of these may include experiential pieces or creative pieces that are related to medicine. There are also many competitions that are linked to the completion of certain online courses or sometimes even in-person courses. However, often these need to be paid for (see "Paid 'work experience' and 'educational experiences'" on page 67 for more information), and so as before, these are potential 'extras' to consider and are definitely not required.

First aid courses are great to take part in before embarking on your journey through medical school. They will provide you with some useful baseline knowledge regarding first aid, whilst allowing you to experience an aspect of medical practice (albeit quite superficially) that will prove useful in the run up to (and during) medical school.
There are also various companies that offer competitions for both prospective medical students and those who are currently in medical school. These give you a chance to meet other students, use/develop skills that will be useful in your studies and earn some really great prizes!

PAID 'WORK EXPERIENCE' AND 'EDUCATIONAL EXPERIENCES'

There are many companies and schemes that offer medical work experiences to prospective medical students that promise a lot, but usually at quite a steep price.

Some of these opportunities can be really great experiences to make connections, learn about a career in medicine and have the chance to take part in procedures or simulations that you may not have the opportunity to in hospital-based work experience.

Some of these paid work experience schemes also offer that you can do your placements abroad: some of which are in more developed countries and some of which are in less developed countries. Depending on the locations that are available, there will be different selling points that are unique to that work experience placement, and this is an important part to research and consider before deciding to book on to one of these opportunities.

Depending on the specific company offering these schemes, what you can expect differs by a lot. Some will offer to pick you up from the airport, some will offer accommodation, some will offer a fully-catered stay, while others will only offer the hospital placement and expect you to sort out the rest for yourself. This is all vitally important to look into with critical judgement, and to find out more from individuals that have been on these experiences. What you are sold online can differ from what you actually receive, so make sure that you are aware of this.

It is also worth noting that what you get from these paid placements is often not proportional to the cost. You can often gain enough (and more realistic experiences) from your work experience at your local hospital, at no extra cost.

A word of warning: don't feel the need to pay application fees for certain hospital placement schemes. If you want to do the experience, then that is your choice, but it is not by any means an expectation to pay for work experience. Medical schools understand that it can be hard to find typical hospital placements for reasons beyond your control. Most universities specifically say on their website or during their open days that medical work experience does not need to be 'flashy', and that it can be something as simple as volunteering in a care home and keeping the patients company. Remember that the emphasis is on the reflection of the experience as opposed to the 'name' of the experience.

WORK EXPERIENCE DURING MEDICAL SCHOOL

There is still the option to do medical work experience during medical school, however the value thereof is somewhat limited. Once you begin your journey through medical school you will have the opportunity the take part in various teaching sessions and simulations as a part of your course. Depending on which university you attend, you will begin clinical placements earlier or later in your degree. However, you will begin them at some point, and there will be plenty of time to gain all the experience that you need to then.

Remember, one of the main purposes of medical work experience is to explore your interest in medicine as a degree/career, and to display your dedication thereto. Opportunities for work experience are limited, so if you are already in medical school, you will have new opportunities that are more appropriate for your current level of study:

"I am currently a 2nd year medical student. I saw several cases during which I realised how important communication between the doctor and patient is. For instance, during my GP placement, the GP was struggling to understand the patient because she had poor English. I saw how the GP used body language and drawings to foster understanding."

WORK EXPERIENCE IN DIFFERENT SPECIALTIES

AN OVERVIEW OF MEDICAL SPECIALTIES

There are many medical specialties and departments in hospitals that you may be able to choose from based on your interests. When the time comes to choose which specialty to do your training in one day, your choices will be wide open, and there are so many specialisations to choose from. Take this opportunity during medical work experience to begin this journey and explore all the options that you will have as a doctor!

Each of the following medical specialties have different focuses, with different 'regular days', each involving different routine procedures and team dynamics.

See the following medical specialty summaries and experiences that current medical students had first-hand during their medical work experience opportunities.

ACCIDENT & EMERGENCY

Accident and emergency is often referred to as A&E in the UK, however, depending on where you are and who you're speaking to, it may also be referred to as the emergency department (or ED), the emergency room (or ER), and less commonly, the emergency ward or casualty department.

This department is where acutely unwell patients present to (who haven't made an appointment) when they come to hospital. Most A&E departments are split into different areas – including resus, majors and minors – for the varying degrees of care that patients require.

THE ULTIMATE MEDICAL WORK EXPERIENCE GUIDE   SPECIALTIES

Patients can come to A&E on their own, or be brought in by ambulance, so how busy the department is varies a lot day-to-day. This will also depend on the time of day, with evenings being busier because other means of receiving care (e.g. GP surgeries) are usually closed.

Most A&E departments are open 24 hours a day. However, as a student completing work experience in such a department, it should never be asked of you that you shadow during the evenings. You should be completing your shadowing during the daytime hours, as you would be in any other hospital department.

As A&E is the first point of care in hospital for many patients, the initial triaging and delivery of treatment must be provided for a wide variety of injuries, conditions and illnesses. This can make A&E very exciting, because no two days on the job will be the same, whether you are a prospective student doing work experience, a medical student on their clinical placement, or a doctor doing their job on shift. Patients often need to be reassured more in A&E than they do in other departments, which can make the job of diagnosing and treating them more difficult. A&E can also be very sad and emotionally taxing due to the emergency nature of it, which is a factor to consider and prepare yourself for before beginning your work experience there.

One of the things that students really enjoy about doing work experience in A&E is the busy nature of it, and the fact that there are more often than not interesting and potentially new procedures going on that you can observe.

71

"I was also lucky enough to shadow a doctor at my local hospital for a week, a placement organised through my local trust. I was on an emergency assessment ward, so I saw some really exciting things. I was taught some basics of examining patients, saw a wide range of acute illness and even got to see blood being taken. I did find it quite overwhelming – this is normal! Try and befriend F1s and F2s if you can. These are doctors who have just graduated from medical school, and remember what it is like to be on a busy ward for the first time."

Another thing that work experience students really enjoy about A&E as a work experience placement is the range that you will experience each day on placement. This includes the range of conditions that will be presenting, the range of procedures you will see and the range of doctors/healthcare professionals that you will be able to shadow. A&E is also a great place to observe a much more fast-paced and efficient team dynamic, as each professional has their part to play in quick and thorough management of very unwell patients.

"In A&E I was able to see a greater variety of conditions. I spent one of the two days in the paediatric section. I also shadowed clinicians of a range of grades (from FY2 to consultant). I was able to observe lots of patient consultations and see how a multidisciplinary team functions."

"I helped to process samples for a trial of certain devices which are now being used in a lot of A&E departments and labs... I would go to Resus whenever a patient could potentially be used in the trial. This allowed me to observe the treatment of gunshot wounds, stabbings, pneumothorax and severe head injuries."

ADULT GENERAL MEDICINE

Adult general medicine is, broadly speaking, doctors that treat individuals that are 18 years or older, with a variety of complaints that are usually more general and less attributable to a single cause. As these doctors treat individuals who are just out of childhood (i.e. 18 years old) to individuals who are older and frail, their knowledge of conditions and treatments need to be very broad, but equally, relatively in depth.

Adult general medicine tend to treat patients a lot in terms of maintaining good health. For example, making lifestyle changes and following up these changes to check that their health is improving as would be expected. There is significant overlap between general practice and adult general medicine, however, most people tend to agree that adult general medicine focuses on the internal medicine side, while GPs are your first contact for any medical presentations. This does mean that the conditions treated in adult general medicine are often chronic and typically less 'exciting' to observe as a work experience student:

"I did one week in the adult general medicine department, which was okay, but limited. The presenting conditions were quite varied, but nothing too serious or complicated, as they were sent to specialist departments for treatment."

ALTERNATIVE MEDICINE

Alternative medicine is medical treatments that are used instead of the more traditional treatments, or in other words, the treatments that are outside of mainstream healthcare practices or standard medical care. In the UK, these types of interventions or treatments are referred to as CAMs, which stands for complementary and alternative medicines.

Alternative medicine treatments are quite well-known or well-heard-of, and you may not have realised that some of them are actually classified as 'alternative'. Some examples of this include acupuncture, osteopathy, homeopathy, aromatherapy, meditation, yoga, body movement therapies and many more. Therefore, some students that have completed work experience placements in alternative medicine have realised that their uncertainty and apprehension regarding what their placement would actually entail was very quickly ameliorated due to the familiarity of so many types of therapies that are in reality classed as alternative therapies:

"My time learning about acupuncture and watching it being done was a really interesting experience. It was so different to what I had expected, as I was quite apprehensive about it all before my placement, but I quickly realised now much like all other treatments it is."

Students that have completed a work experience placement in an alternative medicine setting also often find that they are pleasantly surprised by the evidence base behind so many of the therapies, and the real passion that the professionals they are shadowing often exhibit:

"It was great to hear about the origins of many types of alternative medicine, and what they are based on. It turns out there is actually quite a lot of evidence and science behind these types of treatments, and lots that you need to learn – it's not as superficial as I had previously thought!"

ANAESTHETICS

Anaesthetics is a specialty that is involved during certain procedures, tests and surgeries to induce anaesthesia, which is a temporary loss of sensation or awareness.

Anaesthetists (doctors that have specialised in anaesthetics) are a very important part of surgical teams, and are in charge of putting the patients to sleep, ensuring the patient's cannot feel any pain, controlling the level of drug administration throughout the procedure to make sure it is not too much or too little, maintaining the patient's airway, monitoring the patient's vitals and so much more.

There are four main types of anaesthetics: general anaesthesia, regional anaesthesia, sedation and local anaesthesia. Some types of anaesthesia are clearly more appropriate for certain procedures, but three are some cases in which patients are able to be involved in this decision making process.

A major part of anaesthetics is understanding and having a good control of the pathophysiology of the human body. This is because one needs to know how each mechanism works, and what the effects of certain drugs, manipulations and surgical procedures will have on the patient that they are monitoring. This means that most anaesthetists really like science, and enjoy learning about every intricacy of the mechanisms involved in maintaining homeostasis in the human body. This also means that anaesthetists are very knowledgeable, and because of the nature of monitoring patients and constantly making changes, they are able to teach you a great deal about what they are doing. So, if you get the chance to shadow an anaesthetist, make sure that you ask lots of questions and ask them to explain or describe anything that you are confused about or interested in.

Due to the nature of the work of anaesthetists, they are often involved in a wide range of different surgeries that are done by surgeons from different specialties. This means that anaesthetists will have experience of observing and working with many different types of doctors; so this may be a great opportunity to gain some insight into many different specialties from the perspective of someone not actively practicing said specialty. This does also mean that if you are shadowing an anaesthetist this exposure to different surgeries from different specialties would be available to you too. Perhaps you could even approach the surgeons of different specialties (within reason) to ask a few questions:

"I spent one week in the anaesthetics department, which included a rotating schedule of shadowing in various divisions of medicine and surgery including oncology, obstetrics and gynaecology, osteopathy, emergency medicine, intensive care, geriatrics, radiology and many others. I spent time with many members of staff, ranging from consultants to FY1s to nurses, which I found gave me a comprehensive experience of the roles in the hospital and how they are linked in the multidisciplinary team. I did spend some time with some particularly engaging consultants who directed questions about patients to me. This showed me the breadth of patient care and involvement that anaesthetists have, which as really interesting and a great learning point for me in terms of specialties that I may be interested in one day."

CARDIOLOGY

Cardiology is a really big field in medicine – the heart is a vital part of the human body and there is a lot that can go wrong with the human heart. This ranges from congenital deformities, to heart failure with increasing age, to heart attacks at any age.

Cardiology involves testing, diagnosis and treatment of conditions or disorders of the heart and blood vessels. Cardiologists are involved in the internal medicine branch of treatment of the heart, whereas cardiothoracic surgeons are involved in the surgical branch of treatment of the heart. These areas of 'heart medicine' are then further split into adults and children (which is referred to as paediatric cardiology).

Previous students that did work experience in cardiology found that they enjoyed it particularly because of the variety of bedside tests and investigations that are done, and that they were able to observe. The morning ward rounds are the best time to introduce yourself to the team and communicate your interest to see these being done:

"The morning ward rounds were a great opportunity to shadow the doctors, learn about patients and ask questions. As I was under 16, I was too young to watch surgery in theatre, but I could see procedures, such as ECG recordings, echocardiography and angiograms."

If you are 16 or older at the time of your work experience placement, you should be allowed to shadow the doctors when they go to theatre and observe surgeries. The number of opportunities to do so may differ based on how busy the room is or what the procedure is, so make sure you express interest in this early so that the team can plan for and facilitate this. As you are on work experience, you will probably not understand everything that is going on, but this does not mean that you need to stand in silence and confusion for the duration of each procedure. If you can, ask anyone in the room – most people will be able to teach you something – to explain more about what it is they are doing:

"My favourite part of my week was the cardiac catheterisation lab, where I witnessed a 'hole in the heart' (ASD) repair procedure as well as a TAVI (trans-catheter aortic valve implantation) operation, where I was able to see a live beating heart through a hole in the chest. It was really amazing and breath-taking. I enjoyed observing some of the cardiac investigations, such as ECGs, echocardiograms and angiograms, and learning how they are carried out and what some of the results mean."

There is some luck in terms of the doctors and the general team that you will be working with. However, for the most part, enthusiastic interest from you will be met with helpful teaching from your team. The following experience is a great example of how to make the most out of your placement:

"My work experience helped me get a good grasp of what a day-in-the-life of a cardiologist might consist of. Each day was so varied that I never felt bored being there. My cardiologist was accommodating and was always explaining things throughout the week, for example her reasoning for certain procedures. She made me feel comfortable to ask her and her colleagues questions. There were many opportunities from which I was able to learn about cardiology and the career of medicine. I was able to watch two surgeries, and taught a lot about valvular heart disease and aortic valve stenosis. I even got to see how stress echocardiograms are performed. What I found to be insightful was being able to sit-in several multidisciplinary meetings. I was unaware of multidisciplinary meeting prior to having work experience, so being able to witness one was a big learning moment for me."

ENDOCRINOLOGY

Endocrinology is a specialty that studies, diagnoses and treats individuals with hormone problems, imbalances, deficiencies, etc. Hormones are chemicals that work as messengers to regulate/change/affect different 'jobs' in our bodies. Therefore, they play a vital role in maintaining balance to allow us to survive.

Hormones are a very interesting part of medicine because although you cannot see them, they play a role in almost every aspect of our health and wellbeing. Hormones control our temperature, our sleep, our growth, our energy levels, our mood, our stress, our hunger, our thirst and so much more. Endocrinologists therefore diagnose and treat a wide variety of conditions; from thyroid diseases to diabetes to metabolic disorders to infertility:

"I got to see patients with thyroid problems who are trying to get pregnant or who have recently fallen pregnant. It is important for women with both hyperthyroidism and hypothyroidism to be carefully monitored during their pregnancy to make sure that their levels of thyroid hormones are optimal for their baby's development. It was really interesting how everything is linked in medicine, and how a quick blood test can improve the health of the mother and baby."

With endocrinology, as with any other specialty, there is a lot of science behind each presenting condition, behind the mechanism of each medication and behind each decision that the doctor makes to treat the patient. With endocrinology especially, everything can seem a little bit abstract because we cannot usually see what has gone wrong (usually hormone imbalances). So there may be an inclination to try to memorise the science in an effort to understand. However, given that you are doing work experience pre-medical school, your time will best be spent observing and asking questions that are geared towards your level of understanding:

"I had not really learnt much about this before (and there was no expectation to) so we asked questions and got a sufficient overview that would let us understand what was talked about. In my opinion, time was best spent learning and observing (e.g. teamwork, communication, collaboration), rather than memorising science. Work experience is to get exposure to things that you cannot obtain from a textbook. The days were mostly filled with organising some medical records, observing hospital and community clinics, and having conversations with clinicians about their job."

GASTROENTEROLOGY

Gastroenterology is a very broad specialty, involving many organs of the human body and therefore, encompassing many diseases and conditions. This specialty involves both the normal function as well as the diseased states of everything that has to do with digestion in our bodies: the oesophagus, stomach, pancreas, liver, gall bladder, bile ducts, small intestine, colon and rectum.

Colorectal surgery involves the surgical component of surgeries on the colon and rectum (as the name suggests), while surgeries involving the other organs tends to fall under general surgery (see "General surgery" on page 87). Colorectal surgery is a good specialty to get involved with during work experience if you are interested in or considering a career in surgery. This is because colorectal surgery involves organs that you are likely to be familiar with, in addition to the fact that you are more likely to be able to see what is going on during surgery, in comparison to other surgical specialties:

"I did a week of work experience with a colorectal surgeon, who was an alumni of my school. I was able to watch a variety of colorectal surgeries and the surgeon also helped us get into other types of theatre to see some other surgeries. But I think I was able to see and understand the most about what was happening and why during the colorectal surgeries. During the surgeries we spent time with both the surgeons and the anaesthetists.

Despite not having much prior knowledge on the surgeries or anatomy, it was great to see how a theatre environment works and I was able to make my own decision about whether I really have a strong enough stomach for the surgical field of medicine."

GENERAL PRACTICE

General practice is based in the community, and is often the first contact that patients will have with the medical profession; general practice is also often referred to as primary care.

GPs generally treat patients that present with minor illnesses and chronic conditions that require monitoring. GPs probably see – and need to be able to identify – the largest variety of conditions and illnesses compared to any other specialty in medicine. This is because most patients present to their GPs, who then need to diagnose and treat, or diagnose and refer to the relevant specialists in secondary care.

General practice also tends to focus on the health of an individual as a whole, which involves their physical health, psychological health and social health – and all the respective aspects of that care. As you can imagine, this means that there is quite a lot of pressure on the doctors working as GPs!

Many GP surgeries will have experience working with medical students (at a variety of different levels of training) and may even have past experiences working with work experience students. As GP surgeries tend to be more structured in their approach (i.e. appointments, booking slots, etc.) you may have more opportunities to plan your work experience placement and decide what you will be doing when. Try to take part in the MDT conversations and potentially even offer some of your viewpoints regarding ethical dilemmas or holistic patient care:

"I spent one week in general practice and shadowed one GP in the morning and another in the afternoon. This meant I was able to spend longer periods of time discussing patients, approaches, and the other factors a doctor experiences in their work and life. I also sat in on one of the meetings to discuss the doctors' patients, and was allowed to offer some ethical viewpoints to the conversation. This was a great experience as it gave me the confidence to contribute to medical discussions, and to understand the patient-centred perspective that doctors have. I gained a newfound appreciation for the primary care sector and the stresses which are put upon those who are in it."

GP placements are a great opportunity to shadow different professionals involved in patient care. Often GP practices are slightly less chaotic than hospitals, so you may have more success in sitting in with the other healthcare professionals:

"I got the opportunity to shadow not just the GP, but also a wide range of other healthcare professionals such as a nurse practitioner, an osteopath, and a drugs and alcohol nurse. As a medic, you will eventually be working in a multi-disciplinary team, so it extremely helpful to know about the vast variety of roles available, and this may also be useful when it comes to discussing your knowledge of teamwork in an interview setting."

Another good consideration to have when planning your work experience in a GP surgery, is where the practice is located. Depending on what you want to see and potentially gain from your experience, you may want to pursue a placement in a more affluent area or a more deprived area. You could even plan a shorter placement in two different areas, to give yourself the opportunity to learn about – and compare – the differences. This is a topic that your interviewers will appreciate you having an understanding of:

"I spent a few days in two different GP practices – one was in an affluent area, and the other was in a more deprived area. These contrasting demographics highlighted the huge diversity of the NHS and its patients. I often commented on these differences at interview and I believe this insight contributed to my success."

GENERAL SURGERY

General surgery is the surgical specialty that focuses on all the organs involved in the digestive system, while colorectal surgery focuses specifically on surgery of the colon and rectum. General surgery is mostly concerning the oesophagus, stomach, small intestine, colon, pancreas, liver and gall bladder. Depending on the size of the hospital, breast surgery may be included under general surgery (in smaller hospitals), or it may be a separate specialty of its own (in bigger hospitals).

Surgical work experience placements are a great opportunity to observe ward-based care in the pre-operative period and the post-operative period, while also being able to appreciate the differences between a medical job and a surgical job. Although surgery can be very tense and high-pressure, it is often more relaxed than you would expect. This means that it may be a great opportunity for you – as a work experience student – to ask questions and learn about the doctors' decisions to pursue this career path. This will depend on the specific surgery and the surgeon's preferences, but they are often happy to answer your questions while operating:

"My placement made me realise how diverse the field of medicine truly is. I was mostly in surgery, but I also saw the work of nurses, admin staff, neurologists and radiologists. I sat in on clinics, which helped me see the range of opportunities I will have when I become a doctor. The placement also highlighted how enjoyable and relaxed surgery can be.

Of course, the team was serious, but they were so well-versed in the procedures, not tense and able to create an enjoyable work atmosphere. I was worried about medicine being so intense that I would not be able to enjoy my work, but my placement demonstrated that intensity does not mean that the job will not be fun too."

INTENSIVE CARE UNIT

The intensive care unit (ICU) is also referred to as intensive treatment unit (ITU) or critical care unit (CCU), depending on your hospital and the country that you are working in.

The ICU is the specific department in the hospital that focuses on providing intensive care to patients that are very unwell, and require more extensive monitoring and care. In the ICU, there is often a greater ratio of healthcare professionals to each patient compared to other departments. This can even be one nurse per patient in some cases, where they do observations (more often than they would on the wards) as well as patient care, as the patients are often unable to do so for themselves.

Working on the ICU is difficult and emotionally tolling. The patients that you will see and work with are very ill, many of whom will not fully recover from what they are being treated for. However, it is a great department, with teams of people that work very well with one another, and would allow you to experience many unique situations and cases:

"I gained a new appreciation for how hospitals are run, including all the members of staff that are involved in patient care, the empathy of the doctors and the kind and caring bedside manner displayed. Working in the ICU is difficult, and so you need to lean on each other."

MENTAL HEALTH

Mental health is a topic of healthcare that affects many other aspects of an individual's overall health, and therefore, also has effects on many other specialties. Mental health feeds into many different conditions, and these same conditions often feed into the individual's mental health, which can lead to a difficult cycle to intervene in and treat.

Doing work experience that involves mental health to some extent would be very worthwhile, and a great opportunity to educate yourself regarding the multi-faceted nature of mental health and all that healthcare professionals do in this area of medicine.

Try to prepare yourself for your placement, as you may find some of what you see or experience distressing or upsetting. Make sure that you speak up if you are uncomfortable or have a question or concern, and ensure that you look after yourself and your own mental health and wellbeing as a priority over seeing as much as you can and gaining as much as you can from your work experience.

The following is a testimony from a current medical student about their time in mental health during work experience:

"My placement was at a trauma centre for those that have recently experienced severe trauma in the form of mental abuse, accidents and negative events. The centre focused on care and rehabilitation of these patients before they were reintroduced into society. We visited one afternoon and we introduced ourselves before familiarising ourselves to the patients. We spent the afternoon participating in group activities designed to share experiences, empower each other and normalise the problems facing trauma sufferers in order to recover from them. Initially, I was feeling shy and didn't want to speak, but in order to get the most out of this experience I realised I had to step out of my comfort zone. This allowed me to engage in meaningful conversations with the patients and learn about their stories."

Whether you are shadowing or volunteering in mental health, you will strengthen many skills – for example effective communication, patience and empathy – by interacting with people on this level. Working in mental health will allow you to observe communication with a variety of patients, which may reflect the diversity in the patient population that you are likely to see as a doctor. You will learn how vitally important it is to have empathy and take the time to listen to each patient to understand their needs better and use it to improve patient care.

NEUROLOGY

Neurology is the specialty that focuses on the diagnosis and treatment of diseases involving the brain, spinal cord, nerves and muscles. The nervous system is a very complicated system that has many functions which include regulation, coordination and control of the body's daily activities.

Some of the common neurological conditions that you are likely to come across include headaches, strokes, seizures, epilepsy, Parkinson's disease, multiple sclerosis (MS), dementia, Alzheimer's disease, neuromuscular disorders (NMD) and many more.

Similar to cardiology, neurology is a very broad specialty that encompasses many conditions and illnesses, and therefore can impact many aspects of patients' lives. Neurology is split into various different branches, including adult and paediatric neurology. Take the opportunity to shadow very specialist doctors, to see how many specialties there are:

"My placement was in paediatric neurology. It was a very small department, as it is such a specific specialty. I enjoyed doing something so specialist, as it showed me that medicine is so varied and you can enter into a number of niche specialties. It was sad to see unwell children, but I learnt a lot about resilience in medicine."

OBSTETRICS AND GYNAECOLOGY

Obstetrics and gynaecology (or more colloquially referred to as obs and gynae) is a medical and surgical specialty. This is because it has combined two sub-specialties into one, which focuses on general female reproductive organ health and women's health as well as care during pregnancy and childbirth. Obstetrics focuses on the preparing/trying to conceive, the length of pregnancy, the childbirth and the post-partum period. While gynaecology focuses on the general female reproductive system and organ health, which includes the ovaries, fallopian tubes, uterus, cervix and vagina.

Obstetricians and gynaecologists treat and care for patients during what is often the most difficult and vulnerable times of their lives. Some very important health issues that obs and gynae doctors will help their patients with include birth control, childbirth and menopause – all of which are sensitive topics. If you are invited to observe these discussions and decisions, remember your privilege in having this opportunity and maintain your respectful professionalism:

"During my work experience in obs and gynae, I spent a lot of time in the gynaecology department as I expressed an interest in women's health in my application for my work experience. In the week that I spent in this department, I had the opportunity to observe many consultations, discussions about birth control, treatments for menstrual cycle complaints and unfortunately a few appointments of breaking bad news.

I was also able to discuss how intimate examinations are handled professionally, and the importance of chaperones in this process."

Obs and gynae is a difficult specialty to get work experience in due to the sensitive and private nature of the cases you are likely to come across. However, if you are interested in it, this coule be an incredibly valuable experience that could fuel a passion that may carry you through medical school:

"The obs and gynae team showed a great understanding of patients and their anxieties. One of the main examples that stands out to me is how anxious some parents can be, especially if they are first-time parents. The entire team cared for and reassured both the mother and father throughout the process of childbirth so well. The look of joy and complete happiness of the mother and father as they saw their newborn baby's face was absolutely priceless."

ONCOLOGY

Oncology is the medical specialty that focuses on cancer; and more specifically the prevention, diagnosis and treatment of individuals who have been diagnosed with cancer.

There are different branches of oncology, which differ based on the focus of the administered treatment – the three main areas are medical, surgical and radiation. Within these areas there are also the different types of treatment, which include chemotherapy, radiotherapy, immunotherapy, targeted therapy, surgery, etc.

Try to discuss all these different types of treatments with the doctors and other healthcare professionals that you are shadowing, and find out about their preferences and how it is that they tend to treat patients and why. This is personal insight that is very difficult to gain from textbooks, and therefore, makes your medical work experience a very valuable and ideal time to do so.

Oncology may be an upsetting specialty for many people for different and often personal reasons, and this may be a component that you need to consider before beginning a work experience placement in oncology. However, it is worth keeping in mind that everyone that you will work with during your work experience will be understanding of any difficulties that you may have while being on placement. Make sure that you communicate this with the team you are shadowing and they will do all that they can to help and support you through it!

Oncology encompasses so many different specialties into one because cancer can affect every system in the human body. Therefore, oncology involves many different ward rounds, multidisciplinary meetings, clinics, services and procedures. Your time with the oncology team will definitely grow your understanding of the variety and depth that is available in medicine:

"As I was on an Oncology ward, I mainly encountered patients that were either currently undergoing cancer treatment, or were about to. I was fortunate enough to attend a range of clinical experiences including multi-disciplinary team meetings, outpatient clinics, ward rounds, chemotherapy services and I was also able to observe lumbar punctures and breast biopsies. These experiences gave me a good grasp of the variety that medicine offers (even though I was just doing my work experience in one field of medicine), and also showed me the multi-faceted nature of a doctor's job."

One of the biggest parts of oncology is the involvement of the patient and their family in decision making. There are often various different treatment options – all with their own set of pros and cons, and all with their own success rates. As such, involving patient in the decisions about what it is that they would like done to their bodies and how they would like to function (whether their cancer is curable or terminal) is of utmost importance. Doing work experience in an oncology department will immerse you into the reality of holistic and patient-centred care:

"I would say that the best parts of my work experience were being able to attend clinics and be a part of the MDT meetings. Both of these opportunities showed be the importance of a holistic approach to medicine, and the necessity of keeping the patients' priorities at the centre of every decision made. For me, this highlighted the disciplinary position of medicine as an art, rather than an empirical science."

OPHTHALMOLOGY

Ophthalmology is a specialty that focuses on the diagnosis and treatment of medical conditions of the eye. The severity of the conditions can vary, with the required treatment ranging from observation to medication to surgery.

Often, patients will be referred for ophthalmology review by their GP after consultations in primary care. However, many trusts also have emergency departments for ophthalmology-related complaints, which can be very interesting to do work experience in and will also allow you get an understanding for emergency medicine in general.

Some common conditions of the eye that ophthalmologists diagnose and treat include eye infections, red eyes, cataracts, glaucoma, optic nerve problems, retinal problems, etc.

Ophthalmology has many opportunities to observe different tests and diagnostic investigations, that the doctors will then interpret and use to reach diagnoses for their patients. Take the opportunity to explore the investigative side of medicine:

"I spent a week shadowing healthcare staff in the Ophthalmology department. It was really fascinating. I had never spent much time in the hospital before, so it was a great feeling to gain a glimpse of what a future medical career could look like. My supervisor was a nurse practitioner, who made sure I was well looked after and I was given a timetable to help me gain good exposure to the different areas of the department. I saw eye tests, perimetry, digital retinal photography, cataract surgeries and pre- and post-op assessments. The experience was really worthwhile and helped me further develop my interest in medicine."

The same doctors you observe in clinic will then often also do surgery. Many ophthalmologists love their career because of this variety in each week and even within each day. Many surgeries on the eyes are visible and able to be watched on a screen, which makes observing these surgeries as a work experience student quite easy and definitely worthwhile. As previously mentioned, make sure that you make the most of what you are observing by asking questions to facilitate your learning:

"A highlight during my time in ophthalmology was definitely the cataract surgery; I hadn't experienced surgery before, but seeing the elegance and ability of the surgeon effortlessly removing a cataract and then replacing it with a new lens was remarkable... It really highlighted the intricacies of surgery, and all the different components involved in making a surgery successful. I also learnt about the huge role that our senses play in our lives, and how we are able to process the loss of one of these senses, and adapt by using our other senses to 'fill in the gaps'."

ORTHOPAEDICS

Orthopaedics is the specialty that focuses on the musculoskeletal system – and all of the conditions, diseases and injuries that can affect this system. The musculoskeletal system is a very complex system, with lots of different components that affect each other and which are in turn affected by many different factors.

The musculoskeletal system involves our bones, tendons, ligaments, joints, muscles, nerves and skin. Our musculoskeletal systems play a major role in our ability to move, work, play, take part in sports, be independent and involved in daily life activities – so when something goes wrong and limits our movement or causes pain (which the musculoskeletal system conditions often do), this can hugely affect patients' quality of life.

Orthopaedics is a surgical specialty, so like the other surgical specialties, the doctors will spend time in clinics and on the wards alongside their time in surgery. Make use of any opportunities to attend teaching being given to or by the department, as this will be a part of your development as a doctor, and is also an important aspect to gain insight into:

"I had my work experience at a clinic where I shadowed an Orthopaedic Surgeon. The surgeon was very friendly, and my integration into his clinic was seamless after an introduction and brief discussion on my career aspirations. Cases quickly started to come in, and it felt surreal; I was finally seeing a doctor at work, speaking to patients with so much knowledge and expertise. After the clinic finished, I changed into scrubs to be able to observe the doctor in the trauma theatre. This group of highly intelligent doctors working together as a team and following the lead surgeon's instructions to perform a femur fracture surgery was profound for myself, as a young aspiring doctor. It was all so intense and fascinating. I also had the opportunity to take part in teaching sessions, which showed me there is a constant need for guidance and learning by doing in medicine. By the end of the work experience, I had a pretty good idea about how doctors work and how they interact with patients."

PAEDIATRICS

Paediatrics is the specialty that focuses on diagnosis and treatment of illnesses, conditions and injuries affecting children, which includes individuals from birth through to 18-year-olds. This is a huge range of ages, and what paediatricians need to have knowledge on includes all the conditions adults have that can happen to children too, as well as all the conditions that are specific to children. Plus, paediatricians will need to know how to diagnose and treat newborn babies, while also needing to know how to diagnose and treat – who are more similar to adults in their physiology than children!

Paediatrics is also a very holistic specialty, that works to look after the entire child's health and safety, which includes their physical health, mental health and social health. It is, therefore, a very broad specialty with lots of different branches within paediatrics to ensure that the many conditions and emergencies that can occur during childhood are covered and treated according to best practice. Some of the branches of paediatrics includes general practice, ophthalmology, surgery, oncology, infectious disease, mental health and many more.

Paediatricians are well-known as some of the friendliest and kindest doctors, so you are sure to feel comfortable and welcomed into their team should you do your work experience within a paediatric department. Seeing unwell children may be a new and upsetting experience for many, so as before, make sure you communicate any difficulties with your team and they will be sure you help you in all the ways that they can. Doing your work experience in a paediatric ward will be tough, but it will allow you to gain insight and understanding that will be invaluable during interviews, medical school and into your practice as a doctor:

"One of the parts of paediatrics that struck me the most was the warmth and support of the team. The paediatric ward was so colourful and joyful, even though what many families were going through was very sad. It was very tough to see so many children who are very ill, as I think I had previously thought children were always relatively healthy with the usual runny nose or cough. But so many of the children who were on the paediatric ward were really ill, and many weren't filled with the fun-filled nature I often attributed to children. However, as I previously mentioned, the ward was filled with colour and fun, and the doctors and nurses and other healthcare professionals were really very friendly, and knew how to immediately improve the children's moods.

It was a tough placement, but I think that I have developed resilience alongside many other skills that will be useful to discuss during my interviews and use during my medical studies. Improving the lives of these children during their time with us could be made very joyful, and watching them recover and feel well enough to play, laugh and make jokes again was very rewarding."

PALLIATIVE CARE

Palliative care is an interdisciplinary specialty that focuses on providing medical care and treatment to individuals with severe and complex conditions (that are often terminal). Healthcare professionals working in palliative care work to improve their patients' quality of life, provide relief from their symptoms and reduce their suffering.

Working in and observing on this department is often challenging and emotionally tolling. Make sure you take care of yourself and your needs while completing your work experience in this department. The nature of this specialty means that most of the professionals working in it are very passionate about their work and are therefore some of the best people to have conversations with about their work and their decisions leading them there:

"My palliative care experience included histology, interviews with patients and team meetings. At the end of my placement, I was asked to present a condition that I found interesting, which was a great way to prevent information overload, as I narrowed down my attention to a certain area. It was also the first chance I had to present my knowledge, which prepared me for my interviews and helped me work on these skills, especially with the feedback and discussion that followed. If this type of activity is offered to you, I would recommend you make the most of it! We had an in-depth discussion of palliative care and the difficulties faced in this specialty; I would advise to try initiate these conversations with clinicians and hear their opinions about their work if you can."

PHARMACY

Pharmacy is a separate degree to medicine, however, pharmacists work closely with doctors in healthcare to provide treatment to patients and to ensure their safety in terms of administration of medications. Pharmacists are very important members of the multi-disciplinary team, and their consultations are very useful in deciding on treatment for patients, especially those with multiple co-morbidities or if they are allergic to commonly used medications.

Pharmacists have a lot of information, and much of it will not be terms that you will be particularly familiar with before you attend medical school. So don't get too caught up with everything you don't know and don't understand, and rather take the opportunity to gain experience in the different areas of each specialty than to gain scientific concepts:

"I had the chance to talk to patients, to observe pharmacists working under pressure and to familiarise myself with common medications. I got to observe in the dispensary for a day, where they are measuring medications and dispensing advice, which helped me develop many skills. It was a one week placement and I was there 9-5, so I had plenty of time to settle into routines."

PLASTIC SURGERY

Plastic surgery is the specialty that focuses on alteration and reconstruction – for medical purposes, restorative purposes and cosmetic purposes – of the human body. Plastic surgery is generally split between two different sub-specialties, which are referred to as reconstructive plastic surgery and cosmetic surgery. Definitions of what plastic reconstructive surgery versus cosmetic surgery differs depending on the country, healthcare system, hospital and even among different doctors!

Reconstructive plastic surgery focuses on restoring both or either normal function and normal appearance – depending on the specifics of the surgery and the patient's needs and/or wants. Reconstructive surgery is most often done for human body parts that have been injured by trauma, or become malformed by a medical condition or illness. Common examples of reconstructive plastic surgery include reconstructive surgery after burn injuries, cleft lip and/or palate repair, breast reconstruction after surgery for breast cancer among many others. Generally, reconstructive plastic surgery is considered to be required medically.

Cosmetic surgery focuses more on appearance and on individuals' desires for their appearance than it does on function, which tends to more commonly be the focus of plastic reconstructive surgery. Common examples of cosmetic surgery include breast augmentations/lifts/ reductions, rhinoplasties, facelifts, lip augmentations, liposuction, hair transplantations and many more.

Plastic surgery is a great specialty to see the 'full patient experience'. While you shadow the team of plastic surgery doctors communicate that you would like to shadow the trauma calls, which will mean that you go with the doctor to the emergency department to see the patient when they present to hospital. You can then continue to observe the doctor treating that patient all the way through to their surgery and potentially even their recovery on the ward if you can. This is a great opportunity to gain an understanding of the full patient journey – something you definitely want to mention during your medical school interviews:

"I did my work experience in the summer after year 12. I travelled down to London to shadow a consultant plastic surgeon and his team. I was very excited but a little nervous, as I had never been on the doctor's side of the patient journey. The first day I shadowed a plastics registrar who was on call; this was interesting because he could talk me through the training pathway and medical school tips. I also got to go into theatre to watch an emergency operation on a patients hand who had smashed it through a glass window. I saw the complete patient journey, as I saw a patient in A&E, in the operating room and when they was discharged. Being in an operating theatre for the first time was a little scary, but unlike any other experience I've had. I was with the consultant plastic surgeon and saw numerous operations. I was fascinated by the need for manual dexterity, bedside manner and diligence required to be a surgeon. My work experience was confirmation that medicine is the degree for me; use this time to assess whether this is the degree and job for you!"

Some students that have completed their medical work experience also say that plastic surgery is a great specialty to do your work experience in if you are uncertain about whether you medicine may be too much for you in the way of blood, injuries to body parts, etc. If you have your reservations, address these early on so that you can then either decide to pursue medicine, or pursue a different career path:

"Plastic surgery is a great specialty to do work experience in if you think you might be (or are worried about being) too squeamish for it. You see some pretty awful burns and injuries, so plastics will solidify whether you can handle the occasionally gruesome aspects of medicine."

Work experience is also a good opportunity to address any opinions or prejudices that you have about medicine as a whole, or any specific specialties. Often the judgements that are portrayed in the media are disproportionate and based on certain individuals or groups, rather than the specialty as a whole. Give yourself the opportunity to make these decisions for yourself, rather than following other peoples' potentially misguided and misinformed opinions:

"I found it really interesting, especially because plastics sometimes has a reputation for being the kind of work you go into if you want to make lots of money giving people Botox. My time in this department definitely crushed my prejudices surrounding the specialty, and made me realise it's much more about ameliorating people's sense of self and wellbeing, as well as helping burns victims regain function. It was also very interesting to explore the history of plastic surgery, and its origins in the First World War, which the consultant plastic surgeon was very interested in and enjoyed teaching me about."

RADIOLOGY

Radiology focuses on radiological methods to investigate, diagnose and treat medical conditions. Various imaging modalities are used to visualise patients' internal structures, which includes soft tissues, bones, blood and more depending on the type of imaging and the contrast used.

Radiologists who work in the diagnostic aspect of radiology can do the scans and the image analysis to provide the patient-facing professionals diagnoses for the patients. This is a great specialty to gain an understanding of the intricacies of teamwork and communication to treat patients well:

"I spent time shadowing radiographers (that take the x-rays, CT scans, etc.) and consultant radiologists (those who report on the images). Although radiographers are not doctors, they were interacting with patients who were often in pain, scared (particularly children) or hard of hearing (particularly elderly people). Therefore, I learned a lot from them about communication skills and the importance of tailoring your manner to the patient. With the radiologist, I was able to understand how medical imaging is used in diagnosis. However, my very basic anatomy knowledge did somewhat limit me."

RENAL

Renal medicine, or nephrology, is a specialty that focuses on the kidneys. More specifically, renal medicine works to maintain normal kidney function, preserve the health of the kidneys, diagnose kidney conditions and treat the conditions by improving daily habits, administering medications, giving renal replacement therapy and more. Common conditions that are treated by renal specialists are acute kidney injury, chronic kidney disease and renal transplants.

Renal medicine, or nephrology, focuses on the treatment of diseases that have an effect on the kidneys and the kidney function. Whereas urology focuses on the – often surgical – treatment of conditions of the urinary tract (see "Urology" on page 112 for more information).

As is the case in many other specialties, many conditions can hugely impact the quality of life that patients experience. Try to speak to a patient that has had a renal transplant and discuss what lead them to need one, how they were coping before the transplant and what differences they have noticed since having the transplant:

"I got to speak to a man who had just had a kidney transplant. He had received a kidney from his wife, and was already improving just 1 day after. This showed me the life-changing effect you can have on someone as a doctor."

RESPIRATORY

Respiratory medicine is the specialty that focuses on the respiratory system, which is comprised of the airways, lungs, surrounding blood vessels and respiratory muscles.

The respiratory specialty works to provide care and treatment for respiratory conditions and respiratory-related conditions. This involves short- and long-term conditions that can affect the respiratory system acutely and chronically.

Given the circumstances surrounding the Covid pandemic, respiratory wards may be less accessible for completing medical work experience on. Additionally, the treatment options for respiratory illnesses often involve breathing devices or treatments that are difficult for patients to tolerate. However, it is important to remember that while this may be the case, the alternative is worse and all decisions to treat patients are made as best as the doctors can, with the information available to them. If you are ever uncertain or uncomfortable, make sure you speak to someone on your team to receive clarity or to have your concerns addressed:

"What I remember most about my work experience on the respiratory ward was when the doctors had to put a CPAP mask onto an elderly lady with dementia. She wasn't able to understand what was going on, and so with most of our interactions with her, she became extremely anxious, teary and violent. It was heart-breaking to watch this, especially because I really felt like there was nothing more that we could do, as everyone was doing all they could. It was a really worthwhile situation to have been a part of in retrospect, because it is difficult to process the fact that they were actually doing good for the patient (beneficence), even though it felt very much like we were not."

UROLOGY

Urology is the specialty that focuses on the – often surgical – treatment of conditions of the genitourinary tract. This includes the kidney, urinary bladder, adrenal glands and urethra, as well as also having a focus on the male reproductive organs and male fertility.

Urological conditions can have many causes, can have many effects for individuals' health and quality of life, and can be acute (lasting a short time) or chronic (lasting a long time).

Urology is a surgical specialty, so you will have the opportunity to observe the wide range of daily 'jobs' that the doctors do, which include ward rounds, examinations, MDT discussions, clinics and surgery. If you have the opportunity to, try and follow a patient through their journey in hospital from before their surgery, during their surgery, through to their recovery after surgery:

"I was allowed to join the doctors on their daily ward round. I learnt about catheters, UTIs and was even allowed to listen to lungs and palpate abdomens. I learnt how doctors talk to patients and explain the medical diagnoses to patients. I was able to sit in on clinics to see some of the less acute urological problems and learnt about the various scans used to diagnose obstructions in the kidneys that can lead to difficulty passing urine.

To complete my urology work experience, I was taken to theatre and allowed to observe as the surgeons inserted a stent to widen the ureter for a patient who had an obstruction that I had the opportunity to meet earlier that on the ward round."

GETTING WORK EXPERIENCE

DECIDING ON WHAT TYPE OF WORK EXPERIENCE

The main aim of your work experience is to give you a good understanding of what you can expect from medicine, both as a degree and as a career. UK universities don't give much guidance about your work experience, except for the duration of your commitment and the expectation that you reflect on your placement. This means that you have a lot of freedom to decide which departments you want to consider and pursue a medical work experience placement in. Based on your local hospital or GP surgery, what is available for your work experience may be limited, but in general, you get to choose what type of work experience you want to do!

One of the decisions you have to make is what kind of a placement you are pursuing next (i.e. community, primary care, hospital-based, volunteering) and based on that decision, you can decide specifically which specialty you are planning to complete work experience in.

I strongly suggest that you should use this time to explore careers and specialties that you already have an interest in. I say this because you will get a very broad overview of each specialty during medical school and foundation training, so use this work experience opportunity to pursue something that you are interested in at the moment and will enjoy doing at this stage of your life.

Even if you feel that you are too early in your training to do anything with this experience, it may propagate an interest that you have, or it may teach you about your preferences and help you to be one step closer to figuring out what your interests and passions are:

"I think my volunteering for individuals with dementia was my favourite work experience, as it didn't begin with the intention of supporting my personal statement. The only reason I continued the project was for the love I had for the residents and wanting to educate others on the hidden condition of dementia."

When deciding on what type of work experience to do, the only specific aim that you have really is that you ideally need to do a wide range of placements – with the goal of gaining experience in primary, secondary and social care. Your main consideration should be: what placements and volunteering opportunities have you done already, and which ones do you need to gain experience in to have a well-rounded application. If you are planning your first opportunity, then think about which one you would like to pursue first, or if there are restrictions on your future opportunities, then plan so that you are most likely to be successful.

"Try to find a wide range of placements, as this will allow you to observe healthcare from multiple perspectives and gain much broader and applicable understandings. Especially try to do a placement and/or volunteering opportunity in each of primary, secondary and social care –these can overlap if you are short on time or struggling to plan multiple placements."

Some students find it helpful to decide on the location or establishment that they would like to do their work experience in before they then explore the options that are available at said location. This may be something to consider, especially if you are needing to travel there every day for the duration of your work experience. Work experience students are also often reliant on others for lifts or on public transport to make the commute each day. If you choose the specific institution first, you can then also research in preparation, to gain an understanding of their focuses and values, which will be a good foundation to have for your first day:

"I suggest that if you are going on a work experience placement, do as much research as you can into the institution to get the best understanding of what they do and why they do it. Through this, you can commit yourself to giving your full attention into their environment and be able to gain something valuable from it. This will help you in your medical school application as the most important part of writing about your work experience is showing that you have absorbed and reflected from what you did and can use those experiences in order to become a better healthcare professional."

PLANNING YOUR WORK EXPERIENCE

The first step in planning your work experience is deciding the time period for which you hope to undertake your work experience. This may be pre-determined by your school holidays or by your 'work experience weeks' at school. However, you have the freedom to decide when to set aside a week or two during your summer holidays, for example. So the first step is deciding when you would like to undertake your medical work experience.

Then you have two options: either plan it vaguely and then find opportunities that fit, or find opportunities that fit and then plan it accordingly. I would suggest that you go based on the first option, and be a little bit flexible with what options are presented/offered to you. Planning a work experience opportunity that is 'easier' to secure may be a good place to start as well, to ensure that you will gain some experience, regardless, and then you can venture out and try to plan experiences that are of specific interest to you:

"Volunteering at a care home is a great way to improve your empathy and compassion, whilst helping out in a much-needed sector and improving the quality of life of often socially isolated elderly people. Furthermore, care homes are often much easier to get a volunteering post at than hospitals."

You can display key skills and characteristics that you have developed through work experiences that are not related to medicine too. Ideally, you will have at least one experience of direct patient care (as this is what you are applying to study and pursue), however, you can definitely supplement your application with other opportunities that you have secured and completed:

"Think outside the box! Work experience isn't all about hospitals and general practice. You can do volunteering work at charity shops, get a job in tutoring or work at a local coffee shop. Having work experience on its own is also good experience for developing your character and learning about working with other people. You can always draw on the things you learn when you write your personal statement and relate them to qualities that doctors need."

The main things to consider when planning your work experience is what types of work experience you would like to have a chance to do and what opportunities are available to you, and then to find the overlap of these. If you are restricted to look locally, this will reduce the opportunities that you may have, but you could also considering travelling slightly further for opportunities that you would prefer to pursue. But even with the most well-organised and meticulous planning, things can go wrong and you may find yourself with a placement that you are less keen on. Regardless of the specifics of the placement, there is so much to learn in every opportunity, and you will be able to apply most of your learning to various other situations and placements in the future:

"Try not to be too prescriptive about the kind of experience you are looking for, as anything relevant to the healthcare setting can be a useful experience and can be drawn upon for both personal statements and interviews. Planning and applying for medical work experience takes time and perseverance. You need to prepare yourself for the possibility that you will not get your first choice, but that you can gain lots from it anyway. Try not be feel let down if things do not go exactly as you had planned!"

HOW TO FIND WORK EXPERIENCE

My top tip for finding work experience would be to talk to people that you know and use any contacts that you have. This could be relationships or links that your school has with certain people or institutions, or individuals that you know through family and/or friends. These people could be really helpful in being able to help you secure a work experience placement themselves, or they could give you other people to contact who may be able to help you:

"Knowing someone does help, not because the NHS are trying to make things difficult, but because this can act as a character reference to ensure you are a suitable candidate, especially when you will be directly exposed to patients."

However, if you find that you do not have any links or contacts, this is definitely not a requirement, and you should have the same opportunities – you may just need to spend a little more time to find them:

"If you have no contacts in the medical field it can seem very difficult to know where to apply to for medical work experience. The main place you will find information of what opportunities are available, where they are and who to contact is the internet. Google can help you find what GPs and hospitals are in your area and how to contact them, as well as any other specific opportunities available. Social media can also be very useful. If you have any helpful teachers, mentors, or heads of department at your school or college, approach them and ask if they know of any opportunities available. It is always worth asking older students who have applied to medicine if they know of any places locally which take work experience students."

Most students have the most success when exploring work experience placements and opportunities that are available locally. Therefore, unless you are set on doing your work experience elsewhere (be it a plane ride or a commute away), try to do it locally if you can. This is because you may have an easier and simpler time sorting this out because you are trying to do so with people that are nearer to home and may be more inclined to help. Also, medical work experience is probably quite an unfamiliar situation, so by gaining medical experience in a place that you are familiar with, you will remove some of the uncertainty and anxiety of this new experience:

"When applying for medical work experience it is usually best to apply to places nearer to your home, not only because it will make getting to and from easier, but you may also have contacts there to help you gain work experience. You can search the internet or google maps for healthcare settings near you such as hospitals, GP surgeries or clinics as well as others such as residential homes. However, it is worth remembering that you are generally advised not to undertake work experience at a GP surgery that you or your immediate relatives are registered to."

If you are very keen on doing your work experience abroad, then you ideally need to have contacts or links to people/places that you can use to facilitate the planning of your work experience. This is because international work experience placements that are not done through schemes (which often cost a lot) are difficult to plan due to difficulties with communication, the distance and sometimes language barriers. If you do not have any contacts to the country or specific place that you are keen on doing work experience in, then you may just need to have extra perseverance to be able to plan your placement, and ensure that you plan it well. Make initial contact with the director of the hospital that you are hoping to do your work experience at, and outline your aims/goals, your requirements, your proposed dates and any other extra information that they may need. Make sure that you are reliable in your replies and in your general communication with the people that you are planning your work experience with. As you are abroad, this is likely to be the only channel of communication that they will have with you, so make a good impression from the start:

"I would contact friends and relatives in a country that you would like to do work experience in and tell them about your requirements and what field you would like to be in. Email the director of the hospital respectively, as you need their approval to undertake work experience. Be polite and friendly in your emails, and do your best to respond efficiently and reliably."

When you are working on finding medical work experience opportunities, you have an easier time if you know what you would like to do and ultimately gain from your medical work experience. This is because this sets you up mentally, while also motivating you for the work that you will need to do to secure your placement. Having this outline in your thoughts will also guide you in your search:

"Finding work experience in hospitals can be a stressful ordeal. Places are limited and there are huge numbers of students competing for each opportunity. However, despite the inherent challenges to this process, there are multiple ways that you – as a prospective medical student – can maximise your chances. The first consideration to have is what it is that you are looking for and hoping to gain from this experience.

Then use your personal network and contacts, apply through online trust websites, let your school careers team know and directly email departments that are of interest to you."

One of the best pieces of advice going into the search for medical work experience placements is to manage your expectations. It is a new and challenging situation that may overwhelm you at times. Try to maintain perspective and remember the bigger picture – all you need to do is broaden your understanding of medicine and patient-facing care:

"My advice is to be prepared. Applying for hospital work experience placements can be a disheartening process. If you notice you are beginning to feel this way, it is important to maintain perspective and realise that you can still gain hospital experience through voluntary placements in care homes or hospitals. One does not need to be directly shadowing a doctor to recognise the importance of team work in medicine or the need for empathy when talking to patients."

CONTACTING POTENTIAL WORK EXPERIENCE OPPORTUNITIES

Emails and phone calls are the best ways to contact potential work experience opportunities to express interest and apply for medical work experience. Emails allow for a paper-trail, which can be very useful to keep organised and on top of where you are in the process at all times. On the other hand, email responses can sometimes be quite slow, whereas phone calls are often much faster. Therefore, it is worth keeping in mind who you are trying to reach and what tend to be doing on a work day. Phone calls may be disruptive (especially if you keep on calling), whereas emails can be replied to when there is time – this makes positive replies to your emails much more likely. Remember to be persistent in emailing when trying to establish contact. Even if you are not getting many responses, don't lose heart and keep on trying!

Remember to plan ahead and leave yourself plenty of time for deciding on what type of work experience to do, planning your work experience, researching/finding relevant work experience and then establishing contact. Especially if this is your first placement, try and sort it with enough time to do it and also be able to plan further placements:

"It is important to plan early and leave time for replies. There is no telling when they will email back, and if you have absolutely no experience, you definitely should not leave it until the last few months before application for university."

Making sure that you stay organised when contacting different work experience opportunities. Remember who you contacted regarding which placement and your proposed dates for each. It may be useful to have a list or spreadsheet to keep track of who you contacted, who responded, what they responded with, etc.:

"The majority of places you contact will be by emailing and calling the various numbers on google. It may be useful to make a spreadsheet to help you track the places you've applied and how far you have gotten along the process."

If you have been in contact with the relevant people before (e.g. career day, networking events, etc.), be sure to mention this in your communications in which you are expressing your interest. Anyone that you can have as a contact could prove useful, either now or in the future. Figuring out who the right people are to contact is also a good skill to have, as this will save you time and hassle, while also showing the people that you are in contact with that you know what you are doing:

"Make sure you contact the right people to simplify the process as much as possible. It is usually best to contact the practice managers for GP surgeries, while hospitals usually have an education centre (or similar) you can contact. If in doubt, contacts can usually be found by googling the hospital/surgery's contacts page."

One of the most successful methods of contact is through the medical work experience schemes that are set up in the hospitals. Often there are information/contact sheets to fill out or there are contact details to which you need to send your application to (see "Applying for work experience" on page 152). However, these schemes are also competitive, so securing a place may be difficult and you may have a better experience if you plan and secure your own placement in an area you are specifically interested in:

"Some hospitals may have work experience schemes which you can apply to, either through your school or independently. You should be able to get hold of contact details or links on their websites for work experience application forms. If your local hospital does not have any information online, try contacting their careers/volunteering administrative team with a polite letter in which you can introduce yourself and explain what you are looking for."

However, regardless of how 'well' you contact potential work experience opportunities or well-organised you are and how much time you leave to secure placements, it may prove difficult to find something fitting and interesting. Be persistent in your efforts (even if you start to feel helpless); very few people effortlessly secured placements without some sort of difficulty. This is part of the experience, and is just as valid to discuss in your personal statements and interviews as your actual experience on placements:

"My main advice in this area would be to be persistent and do not lose hope if the first few places you contact are not successful. It can feel very disheartening if you get rejected from somewhere or get no response, but please bear in mind this is very common and you may need to apply to lots of places before something comes through."

APPLYING FOR WORK EXPERIENCE

Depending on where you are applying to, the process of your application will differ. If you are trying to plan and secure your own placements (as opposed to going through established schemes), it is often useful to 'apply' to these opportunities when you are initially expressing interest in completing your medical work experience with them. What this means is that when you email potential opportunities, you should include: your plans, what you aim to achieve from this placement, include your CV and also attach a cover letter. This shows that you are being proactive and enthusiastic, as well as providing most of the documentation that they will require to process your request. This makes it more likely that you will hear back with a successful request:

"Most applications begin with you emailing to enquire about undertaking work experience at a particular place. You should include a bit about yourself, your medically relevant interests and why you want work experience in this setting. You may also want to include your CV and cover letter. They will then usually send you an application form where you can fill out your details and here you can mention what you want to gain from your work experience and areas you would be most interested in."

If you are applying through a scheme or if you hear back from enquiries and are told how to make a proper application, you will most likely be given a form to fill in alongside your cover letter and CV. Depending on the requirements, some places may ask that you also apply with a letter from your school or a reference from someone who knows you well (and is not a family relative). There may also be further requirements, such as a DBS checks, training days and induction days – so leave yourself time and be patient with the entire process:

"The process can take time, which is why it is essential to start applying as early as possible. After applying and being accepted, I had to go on a training day covering hand hygiene and patient confidentiality. After this, I had to wait for a date which fitted around my exams, so the whole process took several months."

Depending on when your birthday is in the school year, you may be uncertain about planning work experience placements before you are a certain age. In terms of doing the actual placement as a younger age – this is usually deemed to be under the age of 16 –, there will likely to some restrictions on what you can observe (e.g. surgery). However, there is no restriction on planning your work experience placements in advance, for when you are the required age:

Similarly, with volunteering, you may need to do training and organise a DBS check. You want to have been doing the voluntary work for an extended period of time before applying to medical school, so ideally organise this at least a year in advance. If you are told that you need to be a certain age, you can still organise the experience in advance for after your birthday."

Some important points to remember about the application process is to start early, be organised, be patient and persevere! The available spaces do fill up and this happens relatively quickly, so try to start enquiring and applying early if you can. Plus, if you are early with your application, they may be able to process it and offer you a placement before they receive the large influx of applications. Do remember to be patient, whether you apply early or 'on time'; if you don't hear back for a couple weeks, you may want to send a follow-up email or try to reach them by phone. However, if they received your application, they will be considering and processing it, and this can take time. If you are worried about waiting, you may explore different options or apply for a different opportunities, so that you have a better chance of being successful. If you receive more than one placement, you have the privilege of completing multiple experiences! You can also use your unsuccessful applications as learning experiences by asking for feedback about your application:

"Once you have found places that will accept work experience students submit your application making sure to include all the necessary information that is required. If you have not received a response within an adequate time frame usually (2 weeks unless otherwise stated) make sure to follow up your application status. Often it may have just slipped through the system as the staff dealing with such applications are inundated with responses, so yours may have not been seen. If your application is successful, congratulations you have secured a medical work experience place! However, if the outcome is unsuccessful then definitely ask the person contacting you for feedback as you can use this as a learning tool to improve your application for next time."

When the application process becomes exhausting and you begin losing sight of your initial aim, remember how important medical work experience is to make an educated decision about your future. This experience (the application process included) will hopefully develop important skills and prepare you to make the most out of your degree, so that you can really enjoy your future career:

"Applying to work experience can seem quite daunting at first and it can be quite difficult, but it is definitely important because it is important to get an idea of what the job is like before you fully decide that you want to do medicine. Work experience for me strengthened my passion for wanting to apply for medicine because I realised that satisfaction that comes with providing care to others and I enjoyed communicating with many different patients each day."

WRITING A CV

Most work experience placements will require you to send them your CV. You can even show that you are proactive and enthusiastic about this opportunity by attaching your CV and cover letter (see "Writing a cover letter" on page 135) with your first enquiry email. Remember that your CV should only be 1–2 pages in length.

You may have a CV already that you just need to update and finalise, or you may need to start your CV from scratch.

The main sections that your CV need to include are:
- Personal information
- Your profile
- Employment (or volunteering) history
- Education (including online courses)
- Hobbies
- Skills and languages
- Internships or previous work experience
- References

Your own CV is your own CV and you can put it together as you would like to. However, these sections will cover everything that your work experience placement administration team will need to know; to make a decision about whether or not they will be able to offer you a work experience placement with them.

'Personal information' needs to include your name, contact details (email is best) and date of birth (to ensure you are the legal age for this work experience, or will be at the time of).

'Your profile' is a few sentences that describes who you are and what you have done. This is a great place to have a 'hook' for why you are a good choice for this placement and to describe what have planned to continue developing yourself.

'Employment (or volunteering) history' is a short list – with dates – of what you have been doing in terms of jobs (if you have any part-time or full-time job) and what volunteering opportunities you have taken part in. This list is often in order of most recent at the top to least recent at the bottom.

'Education (including online courses)' is another short list – with dates – of where you have been going to school or studying and what diploma or degree you were studying towards. This list is often in order of most recent at the top to least recent at the bottom.

'Hobbies' should include a couple sentences of what you enjoy doing in your free time (e.g. sports, instruments, etc.), and what you are doing to explore your medical interests.

'Skills and languages' should be a short list of skills you have developed, which can be people skills or learnt skills (e.g. coding), in which case you should state your proficiency. If you can speak more than one language, this is a great place to include this too, and remember to also state your proficiency in each language.

'Internships or previous work experience' is a short list – with dates – of which internships or work experience placements you have previously completed. This list is often in order of most recent at the top to least recent at the bottom.

'References' is one or two individuals (who are not family members) that know you well in a professional capacity and can be contacted if the administration team have any questions about you.

It is important that your CV is well-presented with clearly headed sections and a clear font. Use headings to organise the information clearly and relevantly.

Make sure that you are able to support and provide insight into everything that you include in your CV. You could be asked to provide evidence, or just asked about it if you need to do an interview for your work experience. So make sure that your CV is honest and a real reflection of who you are.

Don't get too worried about your CV and how it compares to others. It is often just a box that needs to be ticked to allow the administration team to check the students they are sorting our work experience placements for, as well as an opportunity for the department team that you will be joining to get an idea of who you are as a student and what you are working towards.

On page 134, there is a CV template that you can use to update your existing CV or to begin writing your very first CV!

Once you have completed your CV and are satisfied that you have included what you need to portray yourself well and to provide the admin team with all the information that they need, you can ask others for advice. Ask your teachers, friends, siblings, parents, grandparents – anyone who knows you well and would be willing to help – for feedback about your CV. Having a third party read your CV can help give you an idea of how your CV comes across, and help you make it even better, while ensuring you stay true to who you are.

CV TEMPLATE

(Use this as a guide – there are many different styles and formats):

YOUR NAME
Email: your email here

Profile
Your text here

Employment (or volunteering) history
Most recent date – Your list here
Least recent date – Your list here

Education
Most recent date – Your list here
Least recent date – Your list here

Hobbies
Your text here

Skills and languages
Most recent date – Your list here
Least recent date – Your list here

Internships/previous work experience
Most recent date – Your list here
Least recent date – Your list here

References
Your references here

WRITING A COVER LETTER

Almost all your work experience placements will require you to send them a cover letter outlining your plans, motivations and interests. This is usually the first proper information that they will read about you (after your email), so make sure that it is positive, written well and representative of who you are. Your cover letter should convey your enthusiasm and willingness to learn. It shows that you are interested in what you are applying for – in this case, medical work experience.

Alongside your cover letter, you will often be asked for your CV (see "Writing a CV" on page 131). A cover letter is a less formal introduction (in comparison to your CV) about who you are and what you are doing now as well as what you are planning to do. Remember that your cover letter should not be longer than 1 page in length.

You may have a letter outlining your motivation to do medical work experience already, or perhaps a personal statement that can be slightly altered and used as a cover letter. However, if you don't have any such letter or statement, you should find that writing it will be relatively easy if you are genuinely interested in and excited about studying medicine! Plus, it may fuel your passion and motivation to work towards this challenging – but incredibly worthwhile – career.

Make your cover letter interesting and enthusiastic, and most of all, make it genuine. This is reflecting who you are, so make sure it is a well-written letter that reflects you well!

The main points that you cover letter needs to address is:

- Who you are
- What you are currently doing
- What you want to do
- Why you want to do this medical work experience
- What makes you a good candidate for this
- What you are doing to prepare yourself
- What you are planning to do to prepare yourself

As your cover letter is demonstrating who you are to the administration team, include other points (in addition to those mentioned here) if you think that they will help to convey your enthusiasm and motivation to undertake this medical work experience placement.

INTERVIEWING

Interviews at potential work experience opportunities are the last step in your application process. Not every place that you apply to will require you to do an interview, but what quite a few may ask is that you have an 'informal chat' with someone from the administration team or with the main professional that you will be shadowing. This is often less about being a 'final check', but rather just to become acquainted with one another and align your aims and plans with what the team has in mind and what they are realistically able to offer. You should have fairly concrete ideas about any questions that they are likely to ask you, for example how this work experience will facilitate your plans, how you have shown commitment to medicine and whether you are sufficiently respectful and professional:

"Any interviews for medical work experience will usually be very informal and relaxed. They will use this as an opportunity to get to know you better and confirm that you are committed to the work experience, and that you understand how it will work. It also allows them to prepare your placement and give you a chance to ask any questions that you may want to address. The superintendent or director of the hospital asked me a couple of questions face to face to check how I felt about doing the work experience, how interested I was and how mature I was about the sensitivity of patient details. The main thing they will want to know is how you wish to use this work experience to move forward in your desired career, so therefore an emphasis on your commitment to medicine is important. It helps to have a clear idea of what you want to gain from the work experience. Keep calm and just answer the questions at a steady pace."

If and when you go in for this interview or chat, make sure that you dress formally and act professionally. This is probably your first in-person impression, so make sure that you do yourself justice. Don't be too nervous about any type of interview or chat – if you have gotten to this stage, they want to offer you this opportunity, but this is either a last step in their official process or they want to offer you the best placement possible. Use this as an opportunity to practice your interview skills for when you have your real medicine interviews with universities in the not-too-distant future:

"They want to see that you are keen, passionate, friendly, respectful and keen to work in a team."

LAST-MINUTE OPPORTUNITIES

Last-minute medical work experience opportunities are not what you want to rely on in terms of meeting the requirements for work experience set out by the universities. However, last-minute opportunities are great to take advantage of if you want to gain some extra experience, or if an opportunity to shadow on a ward you really wanted to experience presents itself. It will also improve your university applications, and give you more to talk about in your personal statement and interviews.

Understandably, this uncertainty and waiting for potential opportunities can be stressful. This is why it is important that you plan and secure at least one work experience placement early on – remember that volunteering opportunities count too! Then you can take the last-minute opportunities that present themselves as they come, rather than needing to secure placements out of desperation.

'TO DOS' BEFORE YOUR WORK EXPERIENCE

What you need to do before your work experience differs depending on your specific work experience placement. However, there are a few things that you need to keep in mind and be ready to do and/or provide evidence of in the run up to your medical work experience.

"Finding medical work experience placements is perhaps the biggest challenge."

If you're figuring out what you need to do before your work experience placement: congratulations! You've probably secured a placement – or are close to securing one –, and that's the hardest part completed.

Make sure that you keep on top of your communications with the team that you will be doing your work experience with. Check your email's spam folder too, as emails can often end up in that folder and go unnoticed. If an email requires a timely response, your lack of a response could result in you losing out on a work experience opportunity.

Some of the important documents that you may need to provide for the HR department to ensure you can safely undertake your work experience may include: identification documents, vaccination history and signed patient confidentiality agreements. You may also need to take part in an induction day or half day depending on the institution.

A quick checklist for before your work experience:

☐ Keep on top of any communications/emails.

☐ Ask about any requirements before you can start.

☐ Plan your journeys to and from placement each day.

☐ Plan your breakfasts, lunches and snacks. Make sure you have enough food – the days are long.

☐ Dress professionally (or according to any specific specifications outlined for how you are to dress).

☐ Be clear on what it is that you are wanting to experience and achieve with and during your placements – and communicate these on your first day (your team won't know what you need if you don't tell them).

MAKING THE MOST OF YOUR WORK EXPERIENCE

HOW TO MAKE THE MOST OF YOUR WORK EXPERIENCE

Getting to do medical work experience before medical school is a privilege that you really need to make the most of! Being invited into this setting, in which individuals are scared and vulnerable, and being able to be part of a team of healthcare professionals is not to be understated. It is an opportunity to explore what a career in medicine involves, and whether this is what you want to commit to. Ultimately, you need to decide whether you enjoy medicine! If you're spending time doing various work experience placements, you may as well spend your time well and experience as much as you can.

Think about what you want to get from and achieve with this work experience placement. This can be a very rough idea that you have outlined in your head, or it can be a well-thought-out list that you take with you on your first day:

"To get the most out of your medical work experience you must go in with an idea of what you'd like to achieve. This could take the form of some learning outcomes you write down and reflect upon later. It may also be useful to have some questions prepared should you get the opportunity to ask them."

Introduce yourself to every member of the team, so that they know who you are and what to expect of you. It can be dangerous if someone mistakes you for a medical student and leaves you with an important message or request. Try to introduce yourself to the junior doctors, as they will be able to help you find your feet and introduce you to the more senior doctors (especially if you're nervous or uncertain):

"Look for the foundation year doctors. They'll be the most junior doctors on the ward and will have gone through the medical admissions process the most recently. They will know how you can make most of your time on your work experience, and can also answer any questions you have about what you've observed."

Reflect on each experience that you have – either after each experience or on the day as a whole. To help you remember what happened, it can be useful to carry a small notebook (that ideally fits in your pocket) to take notes about interests, specialties, emotions, questions, etc. Just make sure that you do not write any confidential or patient-identifying information down:

"A top tip is to keep a diary of your thoughts and experiences, as it may be many months before you are required to draw upon them for personal statements or interviews and you may forget some of the content of your placement. This also helps you to recall details of your day that would otherwise have escaped you, and will therefore, facilitate you to effectively reflect on each day."

Use this opportunity to make contacts and potentially even begin to form networks. Try to be open-minded in the opportunities that you are able to get involved with. The best way to make a good impression is by being involved and enthusiastic to learn. The healthcare professionals that you are shadowing will be passionate about their work, and so if you show genuine interest, they will be more inclined to help and support you:

"To get the most out of your work experiences always be positive and proactive, making sure you are always learning; show your keenness and actively pursue opportunities to shadow professionals or watch procedures. Ask to shadow different healthcare professionals to gain a multidisciplinary viewpoint. The doctors, nurses and other healthcare professionals will be more eager to teach you and show you things if they can see you are eager and interested... Use every opportunity to make contacts with clinicians, they could come in handy one day! Also, try to be open-minded; you may find the idea of doing a day of work experience with the administrative staff to be less worthwhile than sitting in on clinics, but this is not the case – you can learn new and vital information too."

You will have time during your work experience placement to speak to patients. If this is not specifically offered to you as an opportunity, as anyone in your team, and they will help you find a suitable patient to talk to. Explain that you would like to spend some time talking to a patient to gain insight into their health and their experiences of hospital, diagnosis and treatments:

"Spend time talking to the patients to learn more about the problems they face, so that you will have a better understanding of why they have come to hospital."

Try not to get stuck 'not doing anything' – there is always something to watch, learn or even do. You need to be active to seek out these opportunities, and show that you are keen to get involved and be taught if the chance arises to:

"Don't be passive while you are there. At the very least, be very attentive and observe everything carefully. This way, even if you did not process what happened at the time, you can still remember and reflect upon it later. Try to be proactive and ask questions."

When you are doing your work experience placement you will be treated as an 'adult learner'. This means that you are in charge of your learning, and essentially, what you gain from your experience will be proportionate to the effort that you put into it:

"It was quite a busy hospital, so no one was supervising us to the level we had often experienced in school. This essentially meant the experience was what we wanted to make of it; there was no strict "timetable" and if we decided to not turn up to a designated area there would be no one chasing us up, but equally no one would catch us up on anything we missed. This highlighted the importance of being proactive by asking questions and shaping the experience around what interested us."

Don't approach your medical work experience with expectations that are too high; hopefully this confirms your interest in medicine, but depending on your team and hopes, it may be disappointing or encouraging. Also, remember that you are welcome on the team and that most of the people you work with would love to help you to learn and see as much as possible. But remember that their patients are likely to be a higher priority than you are, and so don't take being put to aside or ignored for a brief period as a personal attack:

"Although it's easy to feel like you're getting in the way, try to remember you have been placed there and work experience is really important to build future generations of doctors. To get the most out of a placement, you have to be confident and ask questions. Most doctors love teaching and want to encourage interest in their career and specialty. Don't worry about asking 'silly' questions – you're a school student so you're not supposed to know about medicine."

HOW TO PREPARE FOR YOUR WORK EXPERIENCE

The best way to prepare yourself for your work experience is to be prepared each day; know where you need to go, what you need to bring with you and what you are doing.

Medical work experience can be quite a shock to the system, because the 'medical side' of healthcare is very different to the 'patient side', and it's often much more fast-paced than what you're used to. But don't let this put you off – all healthcare professionals will be familiar with medical work experience students, and will be understanding of the importance of these experiences for you to have:

"It can be very daunting to enter into a new environment you are not familiar with, however do not let this put you off as everyone has to start somewhere and this is something all staff are familiar with. The more enthusiasm you show the more will be showed back to you, as most healthcare professionals will be flattered that you are showing an interest in their area of expertise. You shouldn't expect to understand everything, as there is a lot to take in! But if there are words you don't understand, do not hesitate to ask what they mean, as it shows you are interested and want to learn."

Some students found it helpful to have a plan going into their medical work experience. Whether this was in the form of a few goals, questions/interests to address or full-day plans, this gives you some control as you enter this new environment. This will also mean that you are prepared to tell your team what you would like to get out of your placement – so being put on the spot with that question is no longer something to worry about:

"I got the most out of my work experience by planning before I was due to start. I created a few goals I would have liked to have achieved by the end of the experience and reading about the cardiology department I was assigned to."

The specifics of how to prepare for your work experience will depend on what your placement and department expect of you. The best way to approach this is to email your person of contact at your placement and ask them what you need to do to prepare for your work experience. Often the reply will be that you don't need to prepare anything, but it's better to make sure that this is the case and that you're not missing anything. There's more information about what you can do to make sure you're ready for your first day of work experience in "'To dos' before your work experience" on page 139.

Some students have previously found it useful to do some background reading regarding the department and/or specialty that they are going to be doing their work experience in. While this is by no means expected or necessary in order to have a successful work experience placement, it may help you to understand more of what is going on and what the professionals are talking about when they discuss certain conditions, treatments or complications:

"I would consider doing some research into your specialty beforehand; I briefly read about some of the most common conditions. Having an idea of what you may encounter will allow you to better process what happens in the moment. You can then focus more on how the doctor approaches their consultations, the difficult discussions they have with patients and explaining the options for treatment. You are not expected to have any medical knowledge, so this is all extra preparation, but I found it helped me to make sense of the management decisions and even impress the people I was shadowing sometimes.

Keep in mind that this will be more difficult if you are doing a placement in A&E or GP though, as the presenting conditions are much more varied."

Most work experience placements for students will be five days a week and will usually start at 9am and finish at 5pm. However, times will vary depending on the set-up of your specific work experience placement. Although this is probably similar to the hours that you go to school (and you're therefore probably used to them), working in healthcare is tiring – even if you are just observing as a medical work experience student.

Make sure that you prepare yourself 'personally' to make your placement as successful as possible. Go to bed early the night before and wake up with plenty of time to get ready and travel to your placement. Ensure that you do not skip breakfast, and consider whether it may be easier to take lunch with you, as the breaks are often not very long. Arrive at your placement wearing the dress code that was specified to you; unless otherwise stated, this is usually smart casual. If you have been given a visitor or ID badge, make sure to have it on you at all times to be able to identify yourself. Make sure to stay hydrated and to eat enough to sustain you through the day. If you are ever feeling uncomfortable or uncertain in a situation, make sure that you say something and ask for help or support.

WHAT TO EXPECT ON THE FIRST DAY

You might be worried about your first day of medical work experience, and that's completely fine! It's a new environment and it's normal to be a little nervous about what to expect and about how your day is going to go. Although no two medical work experiences will be the exact same, there are a few common things that you can expect from most of them on your first day.

Assuming you have communicated well with the team that you will be joining (see also "How to prepare for your work experience" on page 146), you will know where to go on your first day and what to bring with you. If you don't know these details yet, please try to get in touch with the administration team or with your department team to find out these details as soon as possible. By knowing where you need to go and what you need to bring with you, this will take some of the pressure off on your first day, and you can focus on familiarising yourself with the placement and the team:

"As a school student, doing work experience can feel fairly daunting, as you might feel out-of-place or in the way, and you might not understand much of the medical information you're seeing and experiencing. I know this was how I felt at first! However, you can learn so much from work experience and really enjoy it."

Of course this cannot be true for all placements, but as a general guide, you can expect to meet the person or people you had planned with to meet at the appointed location and at the appointed time. Make sure that you are slightly early – or at the least on time – for your first day (and all the days). You will probably then be told where you can leave your personal items and then be given a short tour of the department or hospital (if you didn't have an induction or training session). You will also be introduced to the department team that you will be with for the duration of your work experience placement.

This may seem overwhelming, but you will adjust within a couple of days and then it will all become familiar to you. Do your best to remember the main locations that you will need to know and the main faces that you will be interacting with – and then you can then go from there! Everyone will be happy to help you if you ask, and they're all much more likely to remember you (as you will be the new work experience student), and they'll be looking out to make sure you're doing alright and that you're on the right track:

"It can feel quite daunting when you arrive and may take a day or two adjust. One of the best ways to get off to a good start and give you peace of mind is to arrive slightly early on your first day. Remember to introduce yourself to everyone and try to learn the names of as many people as you can. This will make your work experience much better as you will have many more people to shadow, to ask for help or simply to have a conversation with."

How the rest of your work experience runs depends largely on the opportunity itself, but also largely on what you put into the placement in terms of effort, enthusiasm and involvement. See "How to make the most of your work experience" on page 141 for more information on this topic. You can probably expect to be involved in ward rounds, clinics and in observing some procedures/tests. However, what is available and what is taking place each day will differ massively depending on what department and which specialty you are doing your work experience in:

"In observational work experiences, you cannot actually do anything except listen and observe. This can often be boring at times, but one key aspect to work experience is an interest in learning. If you are shadowing someone who is a willing and motivated teacher, you are in a privileged position. Embrace their teaching while observing their manner with patients and co-workers."

The medical healthcare environment is very busy. Remember that the healthcare professionals are there to do their jobs and work to investigate, diagnose and treat various conditions and illnesses. If you find that you have been left behind at any point, don't hesitate to get in touch your supervisor to ask what you could do or who you could shadow. It is best if you take these situations into your own hands and try to find another doctor or other members of the multidisciplinary team to shadow. Introduce yourself and explain your situation and intention (that you would like to shadow them for a little white), and if they are able to, you will almost always be met with help and support:

"I was told to wait for the consultant to finish speaking to a patient and their family and that he would assign me someone to shadow but it was a particularly hectic day and it became clear that he was too busy/had forgotten. Everything seemed alien to me (as I hadn't had any medical training yet), but I knew this was normal and expected. I approached a doctor who was reviewing some documents (i.e. she was not with a patient at the time) and explained the situation. She was more than happy for me to shadow her for the morning."

It is also worth noting that some patients may not want a work experience student to be present during their consultations and/or examinations. Try not to take this personally, as the patient's reasons for this decision is usually because they want privacy, and therefore do not want an unnecessary number of people to know about their health.

Patient confidentiality is also a very important aspect to consider given the position of trust that you will be in during your work experience placement. You will come across sensitive and confidential information. Make sure that you do not break confidentiality, whether you do so purposefully or accidentally.

Some pointers for maintaining confidentiality are as follows. If you are given ward lists with patient information, it is important to correctly dispose of these at the end of the day in the confidential waste bin. You should not write down any patient identifiable information (e.g. name, date of birth, very distinguishing features). You should also not take any patient documentation or any confidential information out of the hospital. If you're uncertain about any situations, ask someone on your team and they will be able guide you.

FIRST IMPRESSIONS

You will have multiple opportunities to have a 'first impression' during your medical work experience placement. You will meet part of the team if you have an initial introduction meeting. You'll have another 'first impression' on your first real day of placement, when you properly meet the team and begin shadowing team members. Each new interaction you have during your work experience is another opportunity at a 'first impression', so make sure that you maintain your professionalism throughout your placement.

"Small things like reporting on time to the right place can help you build a good relationship with the doctors you are shadowing."

The first step in making a good first impression is to follow the hospital dress code, which is often smart or smart casual. You will need to be 'bare below the elbows', so short sleeves (or sleeves that you can roll up) and no watches or jewellery.

"Dress comfortably as you will likely be on your feet all day especially if you're on wards in a hospital. Most doctors wear a shirt with trousers and are bare below the elbows. Watches are not recommended due to the infection risk."

Aside from maintaining a tidy appearance, you will need to remember to be polite and friendly in all your interactions, as patients may not be able to tell the difference between you and other healthcare professionals. For the duration of your work experience (and medical studies and beyond), you are representing the medical profession, so you need to make sure that you are representing professionalism, trust and confidence throughout.

Try to get involved and show your enthusiasm throughout your placement. This can be in the form of asking questions, offering to help or even just listening well and attentively:

"Asking questions shows that you are very keen and inquisitive, which will help you give off a good impression of yourself. This will allow you to make up your mind as to whether this is the career for you. You may face difficulties with the length of the work day if you're not used to it, but you will soon adjust, just make sure you are taking proper breaks. Otherwise, the work should be interesting and engaging, but if you find it incredibly boring, perhaps this is an opportunity to think about whether medicine is the right choice for you."

WHAT TO EXPECT FROM YOUR WORK EXPERIENCE

Medical work experience definitely requires you to adjust to the new environment at the beginning. It is so important for you to do work experience so that you can make an educated decision about whether this is the right career choice for you.

What to expect is difficult to outline specifically because there are huge differences between different placements and specialties, and even between department teams. However, the following are some common experiences which may help you understand what you may expect from your work experience.

It may be an adjustment for you to see unwell individuals in such close proximity, and often in very vulnerable states. The shock of these experiences can get lost in the excitement and nerves of this new environment, but if you feel overwhelmed or upset, it is a good idea to share these feelings and experiences with your team:

156

"A huge adjustment for me was getting used to seeing unwell individuals. Though at the time, I thought I was mentally prepared, the physical reality can sometimes surprise you. I had never been exposed to multiple vulnerable individuals, all with the distressing reality of a cancer diagnosis and a fear of treatment failure."

You can also expect to be exposed to lots of medicine – including medical terminology, medical managements, medical procedures, medical jargon and even medical jokes. Try not to become overwhelmed by everything that you don't understand, but rather, focus on what you understand. As a medical work experience student, understanding anything is more than what is expected of you.

"Another aspect of adjusting to life at work that I feel is important to mention is the amount of medical jargon you will likely be exposed to, if you undertake a hospital work experience placement. My advice would be to remember that you are not meant to know what these words/abbreviations mean, and you can only be commended for asking questions and showing a desire to learn and understand."

Be proactive in how you approach each day. Make sure to ask questions and observe attentively. Try not to just coast along – shadowing in medical environments is sometimes difficult because you may not always be actively involved, and this sometimes leads to a fall in your focus. Use the time that you do have wisely – even if you are passively observing, watch how the doctors work and evaluate how this may affect you and your decision to study medicine:

"Be confident! You are not there to learn about medical conditions and science. You are meant to learn how doctors work and how that may impacted your decision to do medicine, so get yourself into opportunities to allow you to do so.

You are there to learn – find out about what a career in medicine will involve, as well as what is required for the application process."

A LIST OF 'DOS' FOR YOUR WORK EXPERIENCE

✔ Have breakfast and bring enough food to sustain you.

✔ Introduce yourself to the team as a student on work experience, in case they mistake you for a medical student!

✔ Be confident and communicate with your team about what you want to gain from work experience; have a plan for what you would like to achieve, observe or learn about.

✔ Make the most of your time by asking questions.

✔ Look for opportunities to get involved: hold the doctor's notes, ask questions or even help examine a patient.

✔ Try to observe surgeries, scans or procedures. These will be very memorable, and are always super interesting to see!

✔ Shadow a range of professionals – not just doctors. It is important to have a good understanding of each profession's role and how to work together in the healthcare setting.

✔ If you don't have anything to do, find someone and ask.

✔ Each day, reflect on experiences/skills/patient care you saw and form relevant points for your personal statement.

✔ Speak up if something makes you feel uncomfortable.
✔ Interact and talk to patients when given an opportunity.

✔   Consider whether your character fits the personal qualities that are expected of medical students and doctors.

✔   You may find some experiences affect you emotionally; this is normal. Talk to your supervisor or any staff you trust.

AND A LIST OF 'DON'TS'

✗ Avoid trying to learn all the diseases/science and medical procedures – this is not important for you at this stage.

✗ Don't expect to understand everything. Get a general idea of what is happening, and reflect on your experience.

✗ Avoid trying to be too proactive and overly involved.

✗ Avoid using your phone, unless you have been asked to. It seems disrespectful and unprofessional.

✗ Don't be too worried or too intimidated to ask questions – anything you ask will show your interest and enthusiasm.

✗ Don't stay late. You will still learn a lot and need to make sure you have time to rest and recharge for the next day.

✗ Avoid experiences and opportunities that you have to pay for and/or are very costly to you as an individual.

✗ Don't become complacent or lazy and just 'float along'.

✗ Don't take this opportunity for granted; appreciate the position that you have been invited into and use it well.

✗ Never do anything you are not qualified to do!

✗ Don't worry if you do not enjoy your placement – the point of work experience is to explore your career options. If it is not for you, there may be other areas of patient care (or other lines of work in general) that are more suited to you.

ASKING QUESTIONS

Make sure that you ask any questions that you have while on your work experience placement. This time is a great opportunity, where you will have close contact with many healthcare professionals, who will have the best answers (supported by their own personal experience) to any of your questions. By asking questions, you are also showing that you are interested in what is going on, and that you are doing your best to get involved and learn.

You may find it useful to keep a notebook on you so that you can write down any questions that you have during consultations, examinations, procedures, etc. It is also a really good idea to think about the degree and career of medicine, and write down any questions or concerns that you may have. This way you can address these with your team of doctors when the opportunity arises during the downtime of your work experience placement.

The junior doctors working in the team that you are shadowing will potentially have the most up-to-date information to share with you. They will have gone through the process most recently and may be better equipped to answer your questions. For more experienced information, you may want to seek out the consultant doctors working in your department, as they will have been practicing medicine the longest and so, may have crazier stories to share! For anything in between, you may want to talk to the registrars and other healthcare professionals in your team, as they will no doubt all have very valuable information to share.

The following are some good questions to consider in your own time; to lead you to some other questions that you may have; or that you may just want to add to your list:

- What aspects of a career in medicine do you enjoy?
- What do you not enjoy about being a doctor?
- What is it really like to work in the medical world?
- Why did you choose your speciality?

- What aspects of your specialty do you like most?
- How long did your training take? What was involved?
- What other specialties did you consider? Why?
- What advice would you give me about my application to medical school?
- What are your top tips for medical school?
- What was your favourite thing about medical school?
- What are your suggestions for maintaining a healthy work-life balance, coping with a heavy workload and adjusting to an entirely new style of learning?

NETWORKING

While this may seem very early to begin thinking about networking, your medical work experience is a great time to begin establishing contacts that will be useful to have now and in the future. Anyone that you get along well with can be a useful contact to have, and if you follow the tips and aforementioned recommendations, you will find that you get along with almost everyone you'll be working with.

Networking also doesn't just need to be with people that could help you (e.g. doctors, other healthcare professionals, medical students), but it could also just be individuals with similar interests to you (e.g. other aspiring medical students) or even people that you could help in the future:

"I was very fortunate to have exposure to many different specialties, helping me to understand the varied nature of a doctor's role. I was able to speak to several doctors of different grades and current medical students who shared their tips and generally gave a very positive view of their experiences, which cemented my desire to apply for medicine. I was able to get several email addresses of these medical students who later helped read over my personal statement and even gave me a free skype interview!"

JOURNALING AND SELF-REFLECTION

Keeping track of your experiences is a very good idea during your medical work experience, during medical school and even into specialty training! We forget so much of what has happened to us a few days, weeks or months down the line, that by the time you need to write your personal statement or attend interviews, lots of the details of your medical work experience will have been forgotten.

"It is what you learn that is important. No matter what you observe, make sure you learn and reflect on it."

Working within healthcare is difficult – mentally and physically. You may be exposed to some upsetting cases or situations during your time doing medical work experience, and certainly during your time as a medical student and doctor. Being aware of the effects that experiences have on you, and being able to process them in a healthy manner, is a very important quality to have as an aspiring or current healthcare professional:

"My time at the hospice in particular helped me to appreciate that medicine cannot always offer a cure. This is hard to accept, but I learnt that medicine is also about keeping a patient comfortable and helping them to die with dignity and without pain. I consider this to be the most profound reflection I made from my work experience and is something I will take with me throughout my entire career."

Our recommendation is that you have a notebook with you while you are on your work experience. As previously mentioned (see "Asking questions" on page 162), you can use this to note down any questions or concerns you need addressed. But you can also use this to note down some situations that affected you (while maintaining patient confidentiality), and to do self-reflection or journaling during your breaks. This may help your character development, and even potentially give you some learnings or reflections to discuss in your personal statement or medicine interviews:

"Work experience can sometimes be overwhelming considering that it is a completely new experience. You may also see distressing situations unfold or find operations difficult to watch. The best way to adjust during placement is to make sure you allocate adequate time to relax and reflect after a day at 'work'."

PERSONAL EXPERIENCES

Each individual's work experience placement will be different and will result in varying skills and character traits being developed. What you will observe and be involved in during your work experience will differ from what most others will have seen and taken part in. If you get the chance to discuss your medical work experience with other students – during your placement, at school, or at interviews even –, take this opportunity to learn more about the career you are pursuing. The following are some personal experiences of students during their own medical work experience opportunities:

"The professionalism and trust that the doctors, nurses and other healthcare professionals uphold in front of and around patients is truly impressive. The genuine desire to want the absolute best for all of their patients, and the pure dedication the job really shows you that being a doctor or nurse is much more than a job – it is a duty and a true privilege to be a doctor or a nurse.

The mountain of responsibility on medical staff is tremendous and the way they handle it day in and day out is truly something to admire."

Work experience placements in GP/primary care:

"I spent a week at a GP surgery in a deprived area; I shadowed the GP and other healthcare professionals. As a medic, you will eventually be working in a team, so it good to know about the variety of roles available, and this is also useful when discussing your knowledge of teamwork in interviews. The fact the practice was in a deprived area allowed me to see first-hand the socio-economic factors that contribute to health, which is an important area for all prospective medical students to be aware of."

"I spent one week in general practice and shadowed two different doctors. I was able to spend longer periods of time discussing patients, approaches and all the other factors a doctor experiences in their work and life. I gained a newfound appreciation for the primary care sector and the stresses which are put upon those who are in it. I made a conscious effort to record what happened each day, and reflect on it to come to a short conclusion of what I learnt from each day."

Work experience placements in hospitals/secondary care:

"When the doctors were busy, I took the chance to talk to some patients. Working with people is the main benefit of a career in medicine, so this is a chance to see if it something you want to do, and it can also be very enjoyable for the patients. You can also learn a lot from patients by asking about the history of their illness, medications and experiences within healthcare.
During quieter moments I sought out experience in other specialties that I found interesting.

My work-experience coordinator contacted an A&E doctor who let me shadow them for the day.

This was one of the most interesting experiences as I learnt some basics of examining patients and saw a wide range of acute illnesses."

"I was able to see the day-to-day operations of a ward and see how patients are assessed, diagnosed and treated. I saw how doctors work in a detective-like manner to put the pieces of the 'puzzle' together, and how each role in the team is unique and vital. I saw the importance of tests and scans as tools for patient care."

"I spent a week at my local hospital. In my application, I wrote about my interest in the heart, so I was in the cardiology department for the week. I introduced myself to some of the team expecting me and they introduced me to some of the doctors, including the consultant leading the morning ward round that day. Ward rounds occurred every morning and were a great opportunity to shadow the doctors, learn about each individual patient and ask questions. Unfortunately, I was too young at the time to go into theatres to watch surgery but if you are 16+, I would strongly recommend doing so."

"My first hospital experience was a very eye-opening experience revealing the harsh realities of being a doctor. The monotony of every day in working life was seen in junior doctors, as well as the relationships within the hierarchical system of the various ranks of doctors. It was incredibly interesting if you have a doctor who is open to talking to you alongside their work. You get to see how busy and important the jobs of doctors, nurses and medical staff are."

"I think if you still want to be a doctor after a work experience placement, you can be quite confident that it is the career for you! There are things you may see – such as an ulcer that smells, a rude patient or a doctor's frustration. This should objectively be off-putting, but if you have a genuine interest in the medical field and the medical profession, you will also notice the passion in each and every doctor and nurse you come across. That is what keeps you going through the long medical school applications and seemingly never-ending medical training."

"The work experience that I undertook in a hospital was really informative and eye opening. I was given the opportunity to rotate around several different departments including ICU, A&E, endoscopy and orthopaedics. I watched a surgery being performed which was really interesting.

The main thing that I took from the experience was a new appreciation of how hospitals are run, including all the members involved in patient care and the kind/caring bedside manner of each professional."

"I was on an oncology ward, so I encountered patients that were either currently undergoing cancer treatment, or were about to. I attended a range of clinical experiences including MDT meetings, outpatient clinics, ward rounds, chemotherapy services, lumbar punctures and breast biopsies. Cumulatively, these experiences gave me a good grasp of the variety of medicine and multi-faceted nature of a doctor's job."

"The best part of my work experience was attending clinics and MDT meetings. These opportunities showed be the importance of a holistic approach in medicine, and maintaining patient priorities at the centre of decisions. This highlighted the disciplinary position of medicine as an art, rather than an empirical science."

"My work experience was really fascinating. I had never spent much time in the hospital before, so it was a great feeling to gain a glimpse of what a future medical career could look like. My supervisor made sure I was looked after gave me a timetable to make sure I saw all the different areas of the department."

Work experience placements in volunteering:

"My voluntary experience involved spending time doing activities with people in a residential home, many of whom had severe disabilities. It was definitely challenging at times, but it was incredibly rewarding, and helped me develop skills which were useful in interviews and for patient interactions as a medical student."

Based on these personal experiences that previous students have had on their placements, there is so much variation in the opportunities that can be pursued and the learning that can be done. There are three main pointers that I would suggest you keep in the forefront of your mind to make the most of your work experience placements. The first being to embrace diversity and new or different experiences: try to step out of your comfort zone, organise placements that will allow you to do so and talk to people you wouldn't usually have the opportunity to talk to. Secondly, make your work experience fun by asking to watch procedures or surgeries. You won't learn as much from this, but it may stir a passion in you for a specific specialty or medicine as a whole and this is also a very valuable learning point. Finally, make sure you critically observe the interactions of doctors and patients, of doctors and doctors, and of doctors and their team. Understand how interpersonal skills play a huge role in effective communication and patient care, and reflect on this at every opportunity.

"WHAT WOULD I DO DIFFERENTLY?"

Your medical work experience placements are opportunities for you to experience what working in the medical field is like from a more realistic point of view than that you will have received from the media, from TV shows or even from being a patient. There is always going to be something that you will have done differently (or better) were you to do the work experience placement again. So, the following are some students' reflections on their work experience placements, and retrospectively, what they would have done differently:

"One of my learning points for next time would be to be less nervous and ask more questions to the staff about what specifically they liked and disliked about their jobs, as well as raise any queries that I had regarding why they were giving specific treatments and medications to certain patients. There was so many positives from my work experience, I was able to learn so much about the NHS, cardiology and life as a doctor. I observed teamwork, communication and empathy, and their importance in becoming a good doctor.

When I went into an unfamiliar situation, I tried my best to keep an open mind and to take part in the new opportunities."

"Personally, I do not feel like I had any bad learning points. On occasion I did feel slightly squeamish (for example when watching a biopsy), but I think this is to be expected as it's an unfamiliar environment to be in. With work experience, I think that if one does have a bad experience, it is a blessing in disguise as it perhaps serves as an early life lesson that this particular field may not be for you and there are other avenues to direct you to."

"I would say every learning point is a good learning point, as even negative aspects can teach you lessons if you reframe it in that sense – and budding medical students would do well to have this growth mentality.
I would say I focused more on the technical aspects in the week as I was challenged by the steepness of the learning curve that I was faced with. I could have set my expectations to be more realistic and self-directed."

"I would have approached my work experience with a more critical mindset; to determine if it is the right career for me. If you find that you do not enjoy it, this is not the end of the world – a medical degree can lead to a variety of possible careers. For instance, if you thought the daily life of a GP was boring you may prefer surgery or A&E; look for more work experience to explore other areas. If you no longer think medicine is for you, that is also a good learning point – work experience is meant to give you insight and help you make this decision. Speak to your parents, teachers and advisors about your next steps."

"Ultimately, everyone that I spoke to agreed that the challenges of being a healthcare professional are greatly outweighed by the opportunity to have a positive impact on patients' lives and by how fun the job can be. My placement cemented my aspirations to become a doctor mainly because of how uplifting it was to hear this. In my next placement I will explore other people's opinions on their career more."

"The most important thing to remember when framing work experience in the context of applications is reflection. It is not enough to name drop an impressive placement, and is far more impactful to maturely reflect on it – by outlining what you learned or explaining a change in your previous perception.

For me, work experience showed examples of good teamwork and the multi-disciplinary nature of the career – especially the key interface between a doctor and nurse's role, which I was not as clear about before. No one person was solely responsible for a patient, and so working with the other people involved in their care was important. I saw examples of less effective communication, such as when some of the younger doctors used very technical jargon that slightly confused patients. This is something I would be aware of, and make a conscious effort to learn how to translate the science into information that could enable a patient to take an active and informed role in their care."

WHAT NEXT?

'TO DOS' AFTER YOUR WORK EXPERIENCE

If you are reading this, you have probably completed a work experience placement – and that is a really great accomplishment on your part.

Congratulations!

First things first, thank your team that you were able to be a part of. While most people will be more than happy to have you working with them and shadowing them during your work experience, it takes a lot of their time and effort to teach you. So, it will be much appreciated if you take the time to thank your team and your supervisors, and it will make them that much happier to have had you as a part of their team for the duration of your work experience placement!

As was referenced to in previous sections, it is also a really good idea to reflect on your placement and to spend some time considering what you observed and experienced during your work experience. This will help you to process your experiences much better, and allow yourself to make the most educated decision you can about whether medicine is right for you. This will also make it much easier for you to remember your work experience when the time comes to write your personal statement and prepare for your medical school interviews:

"Learn and reflect – do not leave too much time to reflect on your experiences. Write what you felt and thought while it is fresh in your mind."

After you have completed your work experience, you will also want to consider the impact of this work experience on your next work experience placements. Make sure that you take any learning points from this placement, and use them to make your next work experience more successful. Use any skills or attributes that you developed during this work experience for your studies, volunteering, medical school, future work experiences and any other opportunities. You may even consider asking one of the doctors you shadowed to write a reference to help you secure your next placement:

"You could ask the doctor you are shadowing to write a reference for you for your next work experience, which may help you secure a second placement more easily."

Your experiences on this placement may also affect what kind of work experience you plan for your next opportunity, or for your volunteering project. Use these valuable experiences to your benefit, and use the knowledge that you have been privileged to accumulate to make wiser and more informed decisions in and for your future.

PLANNING FUTURE WORK EXPERIENCE

It is your choice how much and what kind of work experience you do. See "How much work experience do I need to do?" on page 17 for more information about what universities recommend.

Use your experiences from this work experience placement – what you enjoyed and what could have been better – to determine what types of work experience and which departments you may consider pursuing next. Consider the similar and contrasting factors between different specialties to help guide your decision about what interests you and what you would like to learn more about.

You can also use what you now know about looking for opportunities, finding placements, making contact with their teams, applying for work experience and maintaining contact to make your future work experience placements and even medical school placements smoother and easier to facilitate.

Make sure that you don't plan too many placements and put too much on your plate – especially if you are now really motivated after a great first work experience placement. Try to be realistic about the time that you have, and the time that you should spend on experiential opportunities during your final years of school. You know yourself best, and you know what you are able to balance – in terms of medical work experience, exams, a social life and rest. Just make sure that you are realistic about what you are able to take on!

IDENTIFYING GAPS IN YOUR EXPERIENCE

You may find it helpful to consider what gaps you may have in terms of the work experience placements that you have planned or completed, and to use this to make future plans.

The main gaps that you will want to close are any gaps in the basic recommendations set out earlier on in this guide (see "The Basics" from page 9). If it is possible to facilitate, you want to make sure that you have a volunteering opportunity that you have been involved with long term, a community-based work experience opportunity and/or a hospital-based work experience. If you are not able to secure this range of opportunities, you need to make an effort to bridge this gap with other methods of educating and informing yourself about the realities of medicine. Some examples of ways that you could go about doing this includes reading books, following blogs, listening to podcasts, completing online courses and speaking to people who could give you interesting insights or opinions or ideas:

"In order to further your understanding, you can explore medicine in other ways such as through books, social media, blogs and speaking to people around you – this can give you a more holistic idea of what medicine is like and may be more easily accessible."

Once these 'significant' gaps have been considered, you could then give your attention to the 'smaller' gaps. These smaller gaps are not vital to your application or to display that you understand the career that you are trying to pursue. However, they definitely help you to show your motivation, to display more skills and insights into what you have observed, and for you to explore different interests that you may already have in the medical field!

If you have already completed your 'prescribed work experience', but still can't really explain the way that teams work in healthcare or the importance of communication/ empathy/resilience for a doctor to practice well, you may need to revisit your learning. Either you didn't really reflect and think about your placements, in which case do this now and consider these aspects – you should mention these insights in your personal statement and interview. Or you didn't observe this and understand these aspects of a medical career in your work experience, so you may need more experience – potentially in a field or placement that is more likely to allow you to appreciate these key concepts.

Given the structure and nature of these work experience placements that are designed for students pre-medical school, you cannot experience all of medicine. There will be lots that you don't know and have not yet experienced by the time you finish your medical work experience and begin medical school. Understanding the difference between this scenario – where you have achieved all that you can at this stage of your training – and not having done enough during your work experience is an important distinction to make:

"Medical work experience gave me my first insight into what working in the medical field is truly like, and it was only from this that I could confirm my desire to go into medicine. However, it was still limited in terms of the time I could spend there, the location I was at, the patients I could see, and thus, there was still lots of medicine that I was unaware of when I began medical school.

Be aware that your work experience cannot represent the entirety of medicine, no matter how much you obtain, there is still much to explore at medical school."

If you do have the time – for example over summer or during a gap year –, be careful not to get stuck in the more is better mindset. With work experience, it's what you get out of it that is really important, as opposed to being able to rattle off a list of placements and name drop fancy specialties. If you find that you have completed a couple good work experience placements – and you have reflected on them thoroughly and can verbalise these insights – then other than for your own interest/enjoyment or to volunteer, there is no reason to do further placements.

REFLECTING ON YOUR WORK EXPERIENCE

Reflecting on your work experience is very important to ensure that you have made the most out of these opportunities. Rather than just having seen a few interesting procedures and observed a few consultations, make sure that you have actually educated yourself on a career in medicine and decided that you are still passionate about pursuing this degree.

I would suggest doing a small reflection at the end of each day while on your work experience, just to make sure that you don't forget what happened each day and you don't start to get the days mixed up. I would then also suggest doing a longer, learning-type reflection at the end of the placement in which you consider what you have learnt, the skills you have observed and even maybe the skills you have developed:

"Your experiences are only as good as how you reflect on them. Having unique encounters to talk about will really make you stand out from the other applicants – in both your personal statement and interviews. Medical schools look for your ability to reflect on what you have learnt through your experiences, both about yourself and about medicine."

Your reflections may lead you to become interested in or become passionate about certain aspects of healthcare. These drives and motivations are what will sustain you through the long and challenging application process, through medical school and even into specialty training:

"Reflecting on my experience stuck with me the most. The socioeconomic disparities I observed contributed to my drive to pursue medicine. We are privileged with our advances in technology and healthcare; we should use them to innovate and develop the horizons in medical treatment."

Some placements may require you to submit a reflective piece at the end of your work experience with them. This tends to be required by those involved with specific work experience schemes. However, they provide the team you shadowed with insight into what you learnt, what went well and what aspects may need some work:

"At the end of my placement, I was required to send in a piece of reflective writing to the consultant that I shadowed. This is a really good thing to do for yourself too, to help process what you saw and learn more from your placement."

Reflection points that you may want to consider:

- What did I learn about the healthcare system?
- What are the important attributes needed by a doctor to practice well?
- Why is the multidisciplinary team important?
- What skills did I observe, develop or learn?
- What was a difficult experience that I faced? How did I overcome it?
- How did my medical work experience change my perception of medicine as a degree and/or career?
- Why do I want to medicine, now that I have had medical work experience?

WRITING YOUR PERSONAL STATEMENT

Your personal statement is a 4000-character statement in which you have the opportunity to explain who you are, why you would be a good candidate for medicine and what you have done to prepare yourself for this opportunity.

Your medical work experience is great to include in your personal statement, especially if you can draw on your learning and the insights that you have gained during your placement. Remember though, that 4000 characters is not very long – roughly one A4 side –, so you need to decide which parts to mention because they add to your application, and which parts to omit. This is where the reflections that you have done after each placement will be very useful (see "Reflecting on your work experience" on page 183).

Make sure that you only include the most important or most significant insights from your work experience placements in your personal statement. Use these insights to display the characteristics that you have developed and to explain how it is that you developed them during your work experience:

"Ultimately, the people who decide whether you are fit to be a future doctor cannot look into your head and see what you have learned. It is your ability to convey this in a captivating and detailed manner in personal statements and interviews that counts. That is why asking questions are so important. This allows you to gather a lot of personal anecdotes and interactions – which interviewers love to hear about. It differentiates you from people that give general answers and makes you stand out."

As previously mentioned, all of the learning points that you have from the entire experience – from start when you planned your work experience placements, to end when you reflected on them – can be mentioned in your personal statement and interviews. It is also worth mentioning, that if you do not manage to complete work experience before the application deadline, there is still value in completing it. You should mention in your personal statement that you plan to complete it, and then discuss your learning points during your interview:

"It's never too late to apply for work experience, I panicked in the summer before year thirteen that I didn't have enough and I managed to secure some work experience that took place a week before the personal statement deadline. Even if this had been after the personal statement deadline, I still could have mentioned what I had organised, and expand on it during my interview. If you struggle to obtain work experience then you can mention this in your personal statement, reflect on how you tried to overcome this obstacle and how this shows you are a resilient person. You may even mention how you wish to improve the number of opportunities available for students in the future if this is something you are passionate about."

MEDICAL SCHOOL INTERVIEWS

Your medical school interview is your opportunity to let the medical school interviewers understand who you are, assess different characteristics of yours and determine whether you would be a good fit for medicine at their university. They want to choose students that they think will enjoy medicine, and be successful – specifically at their university with their teaching style, as well as within the context of medicine as both a degree and a lifelong career.

"Interviewers are looking for you to have the right social skills, the understanding and the motivation to enjoy medical school and become a successful doctor."

Depending on which university you are interviewing at, the set-up of the interview and the questions that you are likely to be asked will be different. Make sure that you know whether the university that you are preparing to interview at has MMI-style interviews or panel-style interviews. Also, check on their respective websites to see if there is any information about the specifics of the interview set-up. For example, they may give you information on how many stations there will be and what the timing of each station/break will be. You may also find additional information about the types of questions, which may be useful for you to use as a part of your interview preparation.

The main question that you need to prepare for is: "Why do you want to do medicine?". This is a difficult question because for most people, the decision to study medicine will have been an idea that progressed slowly over time. It is also a question that makes many applicants nervous because they want to say the right things and stand out from the other applicants. Think about the small decisions that added up to your big decision to study medicine; brainstorm some ideas (rather than memorise an answer) to have ready if this question, or a similar question comes up. Your observations and experiences during your work experience placements may – and should – have contributed to this decision. Use the insight and the real life examples that you have gained from your placements to build a strong and genuine answer to this question, so that it is representative of your motivations:

"It can be hard to answer the question, "Why do you want to do medicine?". I found that when I sat down and made notes of my experiences and why I was applying, my work experience was a big factor which influenced me to apply to medicine. I enjoyed the idea of integrating the scientific knowledge into real life situations to help diagnose and treat individuals but also loved the art of communicating to these patients to help them feel at ease."

Your medical work experience may come up as a part of your medical school interviews. Whether this is because there is a specific work experience-based question, or because you mention it in your answer about the importance of communication in a healthcare setting, for example. The answers that you will give in your interviews will be different from the carefully-constructed paragraphs in your personal statement – your interviewers know and expect this.

It is important that the learnings that you gained and the skills that you developed during your work experience are real and authentic. This will make talking about your experiences much easier and more fluid during your interviews. This doesn't mean that you can't prepare yourself for some potential interview questions; it is a good idea to run through practice interview sessions to help you become more confident in your ability to form answers on the spot. Refresh yourself on the experiences that you had during your placements, and the significant learning points you gained:

"Before interview, go through your reflective diary from your work experience and try to extrapolate some key examples. Reflect on them and have clear/succinct ways to communicate what you saw and learnt. Make it clear that you are not ending your experience after the interview, and that there is still so much to see and learn now and in the future."

You also want to be mindful not to seem over-eager, fake or over-dramatic. Make sure that your answers remain realistic, and to explain how it is that your medical work experience has allowed you to gain realistic insight into a career in medicine. Communicate the good points that you observed as well as the difficult parts that you saw about being a doctor and working in healthcare:

"Throughout my work experience, I was aware of the daily challenges doctors face. In every setting, whether in the GP practice or hospitals, the doctors worked very hard with very long days facing stressful situations. Speaking to the doctors, and seeing them overcome obstacles inspired me. I understand that a career in medicine will not be easy, but after my work experience, I am determined and motivated to pursue a career in this rewarding field."

Another very common mistake that people make during their medical school interviews is to simply provide a list of the placements that they had undertaken – without any case examples, reflections or learning points. This suggests that undertaking work experience was just a checklist activity for you, and that you didn't appreciate the privilege of this experience. It also may seem like you did not make the most of the opportunities to learn from these placements.

Some examples for how to mention a specific experience, and your learning from them are as follows:

"I worked in different specialties including oncology, cardiology and radiology. During my time in cardiology, I witnessed an emergency situation and it amazed me how the whole team came together, under the leadership of the doctor to stabilise and treat the patient."

"I was at my local GP surgery because primary care is a fundamental part of the NHS, and I was keen to see what healthcare in the community is like. One case that struck me was that of an elderly woman who spoke little English. The doctor was able to adapt to communicate with her in a clear and empathetic way."

"I enjoyed my medical work experience and working closely with patients. This motivated me to volunteer in an elderly care home, which I have since done alongside my studies. Working there once a week has allowed me to form close relationships with patients and understand their perspective on their healthcare, on patient-facing treatment and just about life in general."

Another common mistake during interviews is to appear to have already made a decision about your future studies or career, which will make you seem close-minded as an individual. Think about the types of students that universities would like to have studying medicine on their courses – they want open-minded, motivated, kind, empathetic, organised, hard-working learners. So make sure that in your interview, that you discuss situations and use examples that will allow you to showcase these great skills in yourself. But be sure not to just mention all these 'buzzwords' so that you can say that you included them! Make sure that if you're using a word, that you can substantiate it with evidence and with personal examples:

"I admired the way the doctor adapted his communication skills to the situation to calm the patient down and demonstrate empathy by relating to the specific set of circumstances. This made me realise the value of communication in the doctor-patient relationship. Since then, I have also tried to be more aware of the power of my communication skills in difficult situations and have really noticed the benefits of being flexible and adaptable with communication."

How you go about your preparation for your interviews will differ from person-to-person. However, most people will agree that practicing questions in a set up similar to your actual interviews is the most effective way to prepare and to do well. Practice with as many people as you can, so that they can each give you their own pointers and advice based on your performance. Prior to doing these 'practice interviews', it is a good idea to brainstorm some examples for ways in which you displayed interpersonal skills, important points that you learned from your work experience and to inform yourself on the history, current events and ethical principles of medicine:

"Interviews for medical school can be difficult, however I would recommend practising with as many people as possible. Some example topics could be ethics, work experience and determination. I personally got a book which gave me a lot of example interview questions and I made notes for each of the interview questions that were in the book. This allowed me to have strong points for each answer because I had already thought about what I wanted to say, and I was able to express my passion for medicine confidently."

Common interview questions to consider include:
- What was your medical work experience like?
- What did you learn from your medical work experience?
- Tell me about a difficult situation that you observed or had to deal with during your work experience, and what you learnt from it?
- What are some important qualities for doctors and other healthcare professionals to have? How did you observe these during your work experience?
- Tell me about an interaction between a healthcare profession and a patient that you observed.
- Why do you want to be a doctor rather than a nurse?
- Do you think communication skills can be learnt?
- What aspect of your work experience did you find the most challenging and why?
- What was your favourite part about your work experience and why?
- Why do you think you would be a good candidate for medicine? Did your work experience help you become better suited?
- Why do you think we ask potential students to undertake work experience placements?

- Did your work experience change your mind about medicine at all?
- How did your work experience help you to confirm your desire to pursue a career in medicine?
- What do you expect to get out of this degree?

CAREER PLANNING

There is a lot that you can do with a medical degree, even before you consider the need to specialise. Most individuals do practice medicine as a doctor once graduating from medical school, but there are so many other avenues that you could pursue with a medical degree.

Most people go into medical school with a plan to become a doctor – at some point, somewhere and somehow. Within the UK, the career pathway is fairly clearly laid out and if you chose to just continue through the years of teaching and training, you could do so quite simply. Many decide that they want to take a year or a couple of years out of training and teach, or work abroad, or have children. All of these (and many more!) are valid career pathways that you are able to pursue throughout your journey.

One of the nice things about studying medicine in the UK is that as far as securing a job and knowing what you want to do after university goes, you are well supported by your teachers, peers and the NHS. Going into medical school, you may have an idea about what specialty you want to pursue or you may not have any idea or you may be somewhere in between – all of which are perfectly fine. Most people change their minds a couple times during university, during their foundation years and even into their specialty training. So, don't get too stressed (or stressed at all) about your studies or career planning for the time being. Focus on each step of this process, that will (hopefully) lead you into a lifelong career in medicine!

"It can be difficult to adjust to life at work as it is such as big step up compared to studying. However, the medical school does really help you with this transition. At many universities, the second half are clinical years, so you get very used to having to go into the hospital early in the morning and seeing a range of patients with all different conditions. The vast amount of time that you spend in the hospitals and in a medical environment at your university really does help you to transition into the life that you will be experiencing when you are working. And you can start this process now during your work experience placements!"

A SUMMARY OF MEDICAL WORK EXPERIENCE

TOP TIPS FOR MEDICAL WORK EXPERIENCE

Start finding your work experience placements as early as you can. It's about the quality of experience, not quantity.

Be persistent in trying to obtain work experience. Still try to obtain work experience after the personal statement deadline as long it's before interviews. But if you do struggle to obtain work experience, you can mention this in your personal statement, reflect on how you tried to overcome this obstacle and how this makes you a resilient person.

Bring a notepad and pen (that ideally fits in your pocket) for anything you want to note down to remember, check later, ask about or use in your personal statement/interview. Don't write down any confidential information. Keep a diary of what you have learnt/seen each day may be useful when you are writing your application and preparing for interviews.

Remember that patient confidentiality is important. You must not, under any circumstances, discuss patient issues outside of the department or practice you are based in. Be aware that you may be asked to sign a confidentiality agreement. Also, it would be inappropriate for you to see a patient that is known to you socially, whether it be a family member or friend. If this happens you should tell the person who is supervising you and leave the room.
Tell your placement what you expect to get out of it, and let them know if there is anything you would like to do or learn. Don't be afraid to ask questions because you will learn a lot when you ask questions, and make the best use of your time.

Be proactive. Work experience is different from school; it is not the professional's job to teach you, so you need to make sure that you ask questions and ask for help. The more you seek opportunities the more abundant they become and if you get really stuck in you will be able to fully decide whether this life is for you. Be proactive and offer a pair of helping hands at every opportunity.

Shadow the whole multidisciplinary team, not just doctors. Try to speak to a diverse range of staff. Time with other healthcare workers can offer a great insight into the multi-disciplinary approach to healthcare. Also make sure that you talk to patients – remember to be polite and introduce yourself as a work experience student.

Be openminded – it will allow you to make the most of what you see and enjoy the experience more too. Be confident; it may help to practise speaking with strangers beforehand. Be aware that some patients may not want to be seen with a student present. Do your best not to take this personally, and to understand the situation from their perspective as well.

Have good etiquette – be punctual, dress sensibly and be polite and respectful. Be mindful that the person taking you on is helping you on top of their current work. Enjoy it – be professional, inquisitive and enthusiastic!

A SUMMARY OF MEDICAL WORK EXPERIENCE

Thank you for taking the time to read this medical work experience guide. I hope that it has been useful and that you have been able to find the answers to all of your questions, and that it has led you to consider some aspects that you wouldn't have considered otherwise.

Your medical work experience is an opportunity and privilege to be able to undertake, so make the most out of it! Make sure that you read the relevant section of this medical work experience guide for each part of your work experience journey: planning ☐ doing ☐ reflecting ☐ repeating.

Remember that this is your chance to explore this career and decide whether it is what you want to commit the next few years of your life (at least!) to pursuing. If you do, then you can feel confident in your decision now, because you have educated yourself and you understand what you are working towards. If you don't, then that's also a good learning point – you can know that this is not what you want to pursue, and you can explore different career opportunities!

GOOD LUCK MESSAGE

I hope you really enjoy your medical work experience, and that this guide can help make the process a little less confusing and stressful for you. Enjoy the freedom that you have to explore career choices, and make the best decision that you can for your current you and your future you! ☺

REFERENCES

Bma.org.uk. 2021. *Getting medical work experience.* [online] Available at: <https://www.bma.org.uk/advice-and-support/studying-medicine/becoming-a-doctor/getting-medical-work-experience>.

Medschools.ac.uk. 2017. *Guidance on relevant experience for applying to medical school.* [online] Available at: <https://www.medschools.ac.uk/media/2331/relevant-experience-for-applying-to-medical-school.pdf>.

Gmc-uk.org. 2021. *Work experience and doctors in training.* [online] Available at: <https://www.gmc-uk.org/education/becoming-a-doctor-in-the-uk/work-experience-and-doctors-in-training>.

ABOUT US

UniAdmissions is the UK's leading provider of preparatory resources for university. We currently publish over 100 titles across a range of subject areas – covering specialised admissions tests, examination techniques, personal statement guides, plus everything else you need to improve your chances of getting on to competitive courses such as medicine and law, as well as into universities like Oxford and Cambridge.

Outside of publishing we also operate a highly successful tuition division. This company was founded in 2013 by Dr Rohan Agarwal and Dr David Salt, both Cambridge Medical graduates with several years of tutoring experience. Since then, every year, thousands of applicants and schools work with us on our programmes. These programmes offer expert tuition, exclusive course places, online courses, best-selling textbooks and much more.

If you've found this book helpful, or if you would like to find our more about our courses, programmes, and teaching, reach us at:
Website (UniAdmissions): www.uniadmissions.co.uk

Facebook: www.facebook.com/uniadmissionsuk

Your Free Book

Thanks for purchasing this Ultimate Book. Readers like you have the power to make or break a book –hopefully you found this one useful and informative. *UniAdmissions* would love to hear about your experiences with this book. As thanks for your time we'll send you another eBook from our Ultimate Guide series absolutely <u>FREE</u>!

How to Redeem Your Free eBook

1) Find the book you have on your Amazon
purchase history or your email receipt to help find the book on Amazon.

2) On the product page at the Customer Reviews area, click 'Write a customer review'. Write your review and post it! Copy the review page or take a screen shot of the review you have left.

3) Head over to www.uniadmissions.co.uk/free-book and select your chosen free eBook!

Your eBook will then be emailed to you – it's as simple as that!
Alternatively, you can buy all the titles at

Printed in Great Britain
by Amazon

86623598R00119